DAILY LIFE MATHEMATICS
BOOK ONE

Daily Life Mathematics

BOOK ONE

by

P. F. BURNS, B.SC., F.R.A.S.

formerly H.M. Inspector of Schools

Illustrated by

PAUL B. MANN

GINN AND COMPANY LTD.

18 BEDFORD ROW

LONDON W.C.1

Daily Life Mathematics

by P. F. Burns, B.Sc., F.R.A.S.

BOOK ONE   288 *pages*

Measuring; Workshop Drawing; Scales and Map Measurements; Volume, Density and Capacity; Weighing; Time and the Calendar; Percentages; Angular Measurement; Theorem of Pythagoras and Square Roots; The Circle; Wages and Salaries; At the Town Hall; At the Post Office; Special Revision and Reference Chapter.

BOOK TWO   256 *pages*

Measuring; Workshop Drawing; Percentages; Town Council's Income and Expenditure; The Circle; Metric Measures and Weights; Buoyancy of Water; Practical Surveying; Theorem of Pythagoras and Square Roots; Earth Measurements; Time and the Calendar; Sundials; Revision and Speed Practice.

BOOK THREE   224 *pages*

How to shorten Calculations (Logarithms); Interest and Discount; Town Council's Income and Expenditure; Electricity in the Home; Construction and Evaluation of Formulae; Pulleys and other Machine Drives; Workshop Drawing; Practical Surveying, I (Land Measurements); Practical Surveying, II (Measurement of Heights); The Altitude of the Sun; Earth Measurements; " Age " and " Shape " of the Moon; Tables.

BOOK FOUR   256 *pages*

Imports and Exports; Municipal and County Finance; The Nation's Finance; Providing for the Future ; Workshop Drawing; Practical Surveying; Earth Measurements (Great Circles); Triangles of Forces and Velocities; Principles of Air Navigation; Sundials and Nocturnals; Tables and Proof of Hero's Formula.

BOOK FIVE   *in preparation*

Algebraic Symbols; Positive and Negative Numbers; Multiplication; Simple Factors; Division; Fractions and Partial Fractions; Graphical Representation of Algebraic Functions of x; Solution of Equations; Simultaneous Quadratic Equations; Progressions; Numerical Trigonometry; Geometry, Practical and Theoretical; Circles and some of their Properties; Geometry—Three Dimensions; Pyramids, Cones and Spheres; Calculation of Great-circle Distances, and of Times and Positions of Sunrise and Sunset; A Simple Approach to the Calculus; Geometrical Applications; Differentials of Functions involving Fractional and Negative Indices; Exponential and Logarithmic Functions; Differentiation and Integration; Introductory Study of the Hyperbolic Functions.

GINN AND COMPANY
Copyright

First published 1952
Sixth impression 1960
056008

PRINTED IN GREAT BRITAIN BY ROBERT MACLEHOSE AND CO. LTD
THE UNIVERSITY PRESS, GLASGOW

PREFACE

Daily Life Mathematics consists of five books. The course has been planned for pupils beginning the study of mathematics at the age of eleven plus. Its nature has been determined by three main considerations.

First, it is the common experience of teachers that pupils put forth their greatest efforts when they are engaged on work that they realise is worth while, and further that the practical approach and visual methods of teaching are effective means of arousing and maintaining their interest. Second, it is desirable that pupils should have an opportunity of learning something of their place in the universe, and of the social and cultural institutions among which they will later spend their lives as citizens. Third, because of the wide range of ability among the pupils, the contents have been arranged on a concentric plan, each book containing a relatively complete course; for instance, in Books One and Two there is ample material for the less gifted pupils in Secondary Modern schools; in Books One to Four the content is suitable for the average and brighter pupils who do not intend to take an external examination. Grammar school and Technical school pupils do not need the revision and introductory course in Book One; they will find the integrated course in Books Two, Three and Four, a mathematically sound preparation for the formal study of algebra, geometry and trigonometry, needed for examinations of the standard of the G.C.E., which is provided in Book Five. Book Five contains also a simple approach to the calculus for students taking the alternative syllabus in mathematics for the G.C.E., and for those in industry who are aiming at Ordinary National Certificates in appropriate branches of technology.

The books are built round topics and projects, each of which contains a core of mathematical ideas arranged as progressive studies in the different years. These topics may be grouped under two main headings, those concerned with financial transactions and those concerned with space and time. Among the former are such subjects as Wages and Salaries, House Purchase, Endowment Insurance, Local and National Finance, Imports and Exports, Balance of Trade, the Settlement of International Accounts. The space and time topics include Workshop Drawing, Practical Surveying, Earth Measurements, Simple Astronomy, the Construction of Mercators' Charts and their use in Air Navigation.

The mathematical content of the topics is not split up into separate branches as in the traditional courses of mathematics, where arithmetic, algebra, geometry and so forth each has its allocation of time on the time-table, but is dealt with as it is needed. For instance, in surveying heights of objects which cannot be directly measured, several methods are used. In Book Two, two are explained; first, the gnomon or shadow stick method, the method used by Thales to find the height of the Great Pyramid; and second, the geometric square method. Both involve calculations based on the properties of similar triangles, such properties being readily grasped, almost intuitively, by pupils who have done the work on scales and scale drawing in Book One. In Book Three, heights are calculated from clinometer observations. For this a table of tangents is needed, which is constructed from a circle of unit radius as advocated by the leading writers on the subject in America and on the Continent. Logarithms are introduced in Book Three, their essential properties as indices being developed at this stage by the method outlined in the Suggestions for the Consideration of Teachers (H.M.S.O.).

The human aspect of mathematics is emphasised as the course proceeds by reference, in appropriate circumstances, to the history of the subject. An example of this is the account given in Book Three of an experiment, following Eratosthenes, to determine the circumference of the earth. It was carried out by pupils in pairs of schools on approximately the same meridian, using simple apparatus made in the handicraft rooms of the schools concerned.

The books are intended for individual study. It is recommended that pupils should work in pairs, each helping the other to elucidate the difficulties encountered. For outdoor practical work and the like they should be arranged in small groups. For class demonstration, or the discussion of procedure, or the summarising of experimental results, they should be taken collectively by the teacher. In all the books certain work is designed to develop to the full the capacities of the more alert and intelligent pupils. The simpler sections should stimulate and encourage the less gifted children.

Many children at the age of eleven plus have not mastered the ordinary rules of arithmetic, usually taught in the Primary Schools. For them some revision is necessary. The earlier chapters of Book One provide opportunities for such revision, mainly with small numbers. In the chapters dealing with Weights and Measures, the compound rules are almost entirely limited to addition and subtraction, because multiplication and division of quantities involving weights and measures are rarely needed in daily life: such work is mostly academic. The chapters on Scales and Map Measurements, Workshop Drawing, Angular Measurement, the Circle, and the Theorem of Pythagoras, introduce the pupils to new work on the broader aspects of Mathematics which are developed in the later books.

Book Two provides for further practice in the use of arithmetic in the chapters dealing with Measuring—in connection with the purchase and laying of linoleum, and general household repairs; Percentages; the Income and Expenditure of a Town Council; and the relations between the British and Metric systems of weights and measures. In the special chapter at the end of the book there are some exercises on the fundamental rules of arithmetic: these, it is suggested, may be used at times for speed and accuracy practice in mechanical work.

A feature of Book Two is the development of Practical Geometry—two dimensional and three dimensional—through a number of topics: land surveying with chains and poles; the surveying of heights by means of gnomons and geometric squares made in the handicraft room; the determination of the latitude and longitude of the school from simple observations of the altitude of the sun; and the making of freehand dimensioned sketches, and plans and elevations of appropriate objects.

At suitable stages algebraic symbols are introduced informally as abbreviations in written statements, mainly relating to geometrical figures; and graph-paper is used to construct ready-reckoners for converting metric weights and measures into their British equivalents, and vice versa, and percentage ready-reckoners; and in experimental work on the buoyancy of water.

Book Three opens a new phase. Logarithms and the slide rule are used to shorten calculations; numerical trigonometry involving the use of tables of cosines and tangents, replaces scale drawing as a means of computing heights and the altitude of the sun from gnomon and clinometer observations, and the circumferences of parallels of latitude on the earth; algebraic formulae are more systematically employed in connection with problems in geometry and mensuration; and the topic " Time and the Calendar " is completed by an arithmetical and geometrical study of the " Age " and " Shape " of the moon.

It is confidently hoped that the course will prove interesting, not only to the pupils, but also to teachers.

The author takes this opportunity of recording his thanks to Mr. W. Flemming, M.A., M.Sc., Lecturer in the Education Department of the University College, Leicester, formerly Lecturer in Mathematics, Trinity College, Carmarthen; and to Mr. I. R. Vesselo, B.Sc., Senior Lecturer in Mathematics, Alsager Training College, for their helpful criticisms and suggestions when the course was in the draft stage; to Mrs. I. Shelton and Mr. A. P. Davis, both of Messrs. Ginn and Company, the former for the lay-out of the books; the latter for his inspiration, encouragement and help in the preparation of the course.

CONTENTS

To the Pupils

You are about to enter upon a four-year course in Practical Mathematics. You will be curious to know what Mathematics is. It is probably the oldest branch of Science. Many centuries before Christ was born, there were skilled mathematicians in China, Egypt, Babylonia, and Greece, who were mainly occupied in Astronomy and Land-Surveying, both branches of Practical Mathematics.

Just glance through this book—the first of four, one for each year of the course—and you will see that Practical Mathematics deals very largely with affairs of everyday-life: in the home, on the land, in workshops, offices and other places of employment.

You will see that Arithmetic, one of the main branches of Mathematics, is used in connection with most of the topics, but Mathematics is something more than just " doing sums ". When you use a blueprint in the handicraft room, or measure a window for curtains, or consult a map to plan a ramble, or set-out a football pitch, or measure a plot of ground, you are *using* Mathematics.

You will learn to make apparatus and instruments, such as clinometers, sighting-rules, and optical-squares for use in land-surveying; sun-dials and nocturnals which will help you to find your way by means of the sun, the moon, and the stars.

If you are good at Arithmetic, the foundation of Mathematics, you will have no difficulty in working straight through this book; if you are not very good at it, do not be discouraged, because you will find plenty of opportunities of revising those rules which you may have forgotten, or in which you may not be very skilful. For instance, in Chapter I, you need to know how to multiply and divide ordinary numbers, and something about fractions. If you need practice in these rules you will find, in the Special Chapter—on pages 236 to 269— a number of exercises that will help you. You need not do all of them; do just sufficient to remove your weakness.

There are many methods of doing the ordinary rules of Arithmetic: addition, subtraction, multiplication, and division. Some of you will have been taught one way to do them; some another. If you have forgotten the method you were taught, or find it difficult, you are advised to do them in the way shown in the Special Chapter.

Now, let us begin the work of Chapter I.

I

MEASURING

Measuring lengths

On the opposite page there are illustrations of some textile fabrics and instruments which are used to measure them:

an ordinary twelve-inch ruler,

a household or dressmaker's tape-measure (60 inches long),

a tailor's or draper's yard-stick, and

a box-like cloth-measuring instrument, based on the principle of the bicycle cyclometer, used in many drapery shops.

All these instruments remind us of the first part of a table of lengths which we should know by heart:

$$\begin{aligned}
12 \text{ inches} &= 1 \text{ foot}; \\
36 \text{ inches, or} & \\
3 \text{ feet} &= 1 \text{ yard}.
\end{aligned}$$

It is also convenient to remember the number of inches in a quarter of a yard; in half a yard; and in three-quarters of a yard.

A quarter of a yard   = 9 inches;

half a yard   =18 inches (or, 1 foot 6 inches);

three-quarters of a yard =27 inches (or, 2 feet 3 inches).

Tailors and dressmakers usually express their measurements for garments to the nearest quarter of an inch because the materials, such as cloth, with which they work, are likely to stretch when they are being measured, so measurements more accurate than to the nearest quarter of an inch cannot easily be made; that is why the inches on tape-measures and yard-sticks are frequently divided only into halves and quarters.

Draughtsmen, and craftsmen who work with materials such as stone, wood and metal, use rulers on which the inches are divided into smaller fractions of an inch. The inches on an ordinary twelve-inch ruler are so divided: some into halves, quarters, eighths, and sixteenths; some into halves, quarters and twelfths; others into halves and tenths.

1

It is customary when measuring for household fittings or furnishing materials with a twelve-inch ruler to express the measurements in feet and inches. If the measurements are made with a 60-inch measuring-tape, they are expressed in inches. Before ordering the goods in a house-furnisher's or a draper's shop, however, the measurements have to be turned into yards, probably to the nearest quarter of a yard, because the materials are usually sold by the yard.

For instance, how many yards of stair-carpet would be needed for a staircase in which there are 11 " treads ", each 9 ins. broad, and a landing 3 ft. 6 ins. long; the " riser " of the steps being 7 ins.?

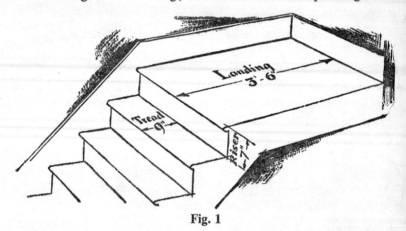

Fig. 1

There are 12 " risers " (one below each tread and one below the landing).

$$12 \text{ risers, each 7 ins.} = 7 \text{ ins.} \times 12$$
$$= 84 \text{ ins.}$$
$$11 \text{ treads, each 9 ins.} = 9 \text{ ins.} \times 11$$
$$= 99 \text{ ins.}$$
$$\text{landing, 3 ft. 6 ins.} = 42 \text{ ins.}$$

Therefore,   total length $= 225$ ins.

Number of yards of stair-carpet to be ordered $= 225$ ins. $\div 36$ ins.

$$
\begin{array}{r}
6 \text{ yds.} \\
36 \overline{\smash{)}225 \text{ ins.}} \\
216 \text{ ins.} \\
\hline
9 \text{ ins.}
\end{array}
\quad = \tfrac{1}{4} \text{ of a yd.}
$$

Length of stair-carpet needed $= 6\tfrac{1}{4}$ yds.

EXERCISE I

These examples are for practice in changing inches, and feet and inches into yards, and *vice versa*.

Change into yards, to the nearest quarter of a yard, the following:

1. 268 ins.	**2.** 600 ins.	**3.** 754 ins.
4. 197 ins.	**5.** 385 ins.	**6.** 1368 ins.
7. 2542 ins.	**8.** 791 ins.	**9.** 4527 ins.
10. 875 ins.	**11.** 476 ins.	**12.** 3841 ins.
13. 7 ft. 9 ins.	**14.** 14 ft. 7 ins.	**15.** 26 ft. 4 ins.
16. 19 ft. 6 ins.	**17.** 22 ft. 10 ins.	**18.** 142 ft. 3 ins.
19. 35 ft. 8 ins.	**20.** 167 ft. 2 ins.	**21.** 91 ft. 7 ins.
22. 27 ft. 4 ins.	**23.** 86 ft. 5 ins.	**24.** 106 ft. 8 ins.

Change into inches the following:

25. 17 ft. 5 ins.	**26.** 24 ft. 10 ins.	**27.** 162 ft. 3 ins.
28. 83 ft. 9 ins.	**29.** 136 ft. 4 ins.	**30.** 286 ft. 7 ins.
31. 27 ft. 8 ins.	**32.** 74 ft. 9 ins.	**33.** 125 ft. 11 ins.
34. 67 ft. 7 ins.	**35.** 91 ft. 7 ins.	**36.** 82 ft. 9 ins.
37. 5 yds. 2 ft. 10 ins.		**38.** 12 yds. 1 ft. 5 ins.
39. 38 yds. 0 ft. 10 ins.		**40.** 17 yds. 1 ft. 8 ins.
41. 73 yds. 2 ft. 10 ins.		**42.** 43 yds. 1 ft. 7 ins.
43. 38 yds. 2 ft. 2 ins.		**44.** 23 yds. 0 ft. 11 ins.
45. 82 yds. 2 ft. 8 ins.		**46.** 28 yds. 1 ft. 1 in.
47. 37 yds. 2 ft. 9 ins.		**48.** 112 yds. 1 ft. 6 ins.
49. 25 yds. 1 ft. 7 ins.		**50.** 15 yds. 2 ft. 9 ins.

EXERCISE II

1. A strip of tapestry $2\frac{1}{4}$ yds. long, 16 ins. wide, was cut into four equal lengths for re-seating chairs. What would be the length and breadth of each piece?

B

D.L.M.

2. Fig. 2 shows six pieces of webbing, interlaced and nailed to a wooden frame to form the foundation of the upholstered seat of a chair. How many yards of webbing would be needed for re-seating six chairs of that size?

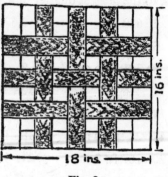

Fig. 2

3. How many yards of braid would it take to go round four chair seats of the size of that shown in Fig. 2.

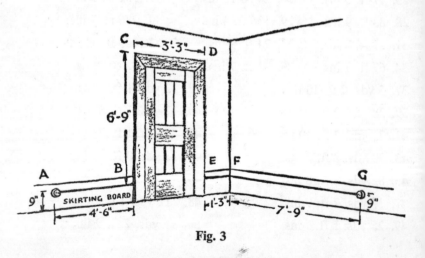

Fig. 3

4. How many yards of " Twin Wireless-Flex " would be needed to connect the plug *A* to the plug *G*, by passing it along the skirting board from *A* to *B*; round the door-frame *BCDE*, and along the skirting-board from *E* to *F* and *G*?

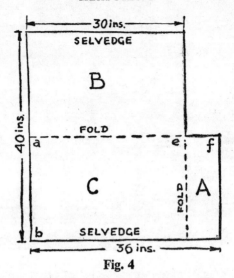

Fig. 4

5. Fig. 4 shows how linen, 40 ins. wide, may be cut to make pillow-cases, approximately 30 ins. by 20 ins. with an inside flap 6 ins. wide.

The flap *A* is folded over *C* and sewn to it along its upper edge *ef*.

B is then folded under *C* and sewn to it and to the other narrow end of the flap, along, the selvedges and the end *ab*. The pillow-case is then turned inside-out so that the hems may not be seen. Calculate the number of yds. of linen needed for six pairs of pillow-cases.

6. Antirrhinum plants are to be planted, 9 ins. apart, in three rows in a garden-border 15 yds. long. How many dozen plants will be needed?

7. Three and three-quarter dozen privet plants were bought to make a garden hedge between two posts 12 yds. apart. The plants at each end of the hedge are to be 6 ins. from the posts. Calculate the distance apart of the rest of the plants in the hedge.

8. In an allotment, a bed, 10 yds. by 6 yds., is to be planted with cabbage plants. The rows are to be approximately 18 ins. apart, from end to end of the bed, and the plants are to be about 1 ft. apart in the rows. Make an estimate, to the nearest 25, of the number of plants that will be required.

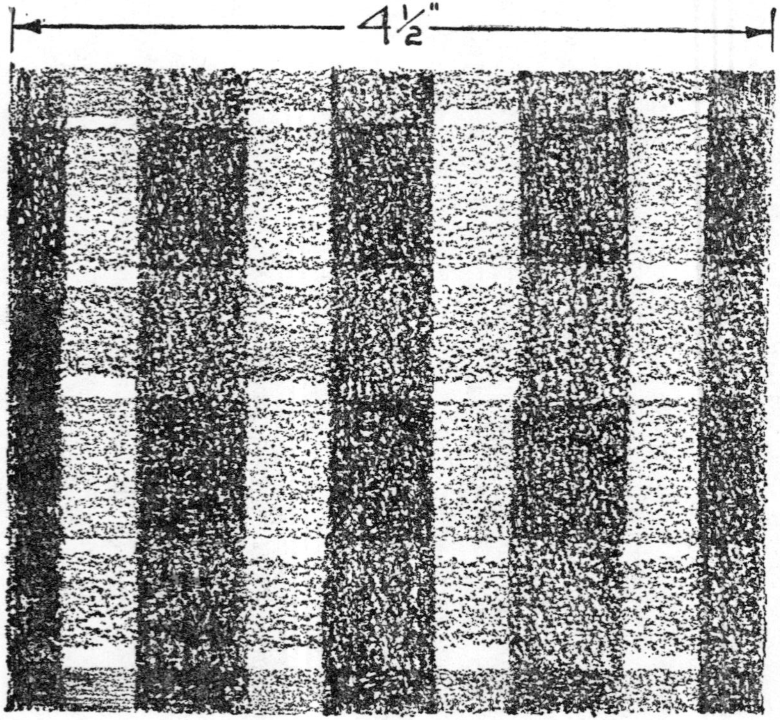

3"

Fig. 6

4½"

Fig. 5

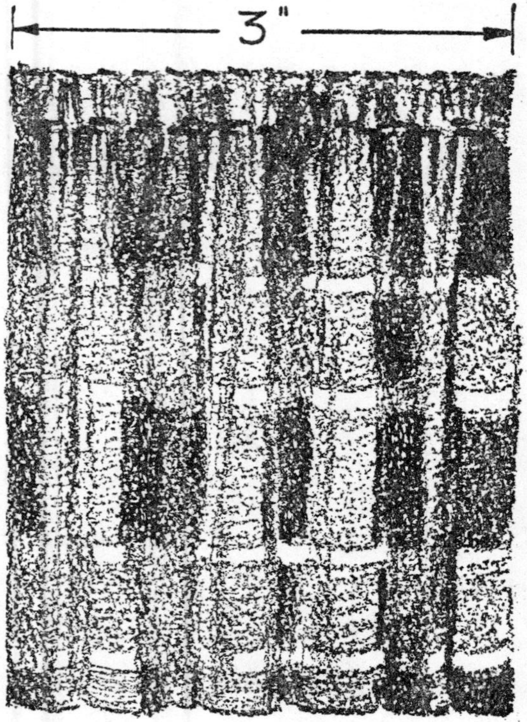

9. The floor of a garage, 6 yds. long, 3 yds. wide, is to be paved with bricks, 9 ins. × 4½ ins. × 3 ins., laid edgewise in rows across the garage, the bricks being laid end-to-end in the rows.
   Calculate (a) the number of bricks in each row;
              (b) the number of rows of bricks;
              (c) the total number of bricks to the nearest fifty.

10. Concrete kerb-stones, each 27 ins. long, are to be laid along the edge of a foot-path. How many kerb-stones would be needed for every hundred yards of foot-path?

11. A staircase consists of thirteen 10½-in. treads, fourteen 6¼-in. risers, landing 5 ft. 6 ins. long. Calculate, to the nearest quarter-of-a-yard, the length of stair-carpet for it.

12. Field-drain pipes, each 1 ft. long, are to be laid round the edges of the lawn shown in the dimensioned sketch below (Fig. 7), and across it in the positions shown by the dotted lines.
    How many lengths of pipe will be needed?

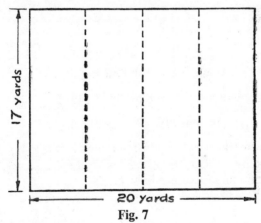

Fig. 7

Making and fitting curtains

Figs. 5 and 6 show two pieces of casement curtain material. The two pieces were originally the same width, namely, 4½ ins., but the one on the right has been gathered to 3 ins. so as to make it drape well. This is the usual proportion used by house-furnishers for draping purposes.

What fraction of the original width of the material is the draped width of the curtain? That is, what fraction of 4½ ins. is 3 ins.?

A ruler will help us to find out.

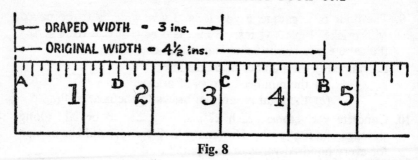

Fig. 8

AB represents the original width of the material; *AC* is the draped width.

The point marked *D* in the ruler is, clearly, the mid-point of *AC*, and the points *D* and *C* divide *AB* into three equal parts, each of which is one-third, that is $\frac{1}{3}$, of the original width.

Therefore,   *AC* = two-thirds of *AB*;

that is, $AC = \frac{2}{3}$ of *AB*.

Therefore, the draped width $= \frac{2}{3}$ of the original width.

We might have done this calculation as follows:

The draped width $= \frac{3}{4\frac{1}{2}}$ of the original width.

Now, this fraction, namely, $\frac{3}{4\frac{1}{2}}$ is rather an awkward fraction to work with because the *denominator* is not a whole number, so we turn both the measurements—the 3 ins. in the *numerator*, and the $4\frac{1}{2}$ ins. in the denominator—into half-inches.

In 3 ins. there are 6 half-ins.; and in $4\frac{1}{2}$ ins. there are 9 half-ins.; so we write,

the draped width $= \frac{6}{9}$ of the original width;

this fraction, $\frac{6}{9}$, is equal to $\frac{2}{3}$, as we can see if we " cancel ", that is if we divide the numerator and the denominator by the same number.

Both 6 and 9 can be divided by 3, so we " cancel by 3 " as follows:

$$\frac{6}{9} = \frac{2}{3}.$$

Therefore the draped width $= \frac{2}{3}$ of the original width.

What would be the draped widths of curtains made from the following widths of material:

Washable chintz	31 ins. wide?
Rayon rep	50 ins. wide?
Casement curtain	54 ins. wide?

Here are two further examples of the way we express one measurement as a fraction of another.

(a) What fraction of 10 ins. is $7\frac{1}{2}$ ins.? Turn both measurements into half-inches.

$$7\frac{1}{2} \text{ ins.} = 15 \text{ half-ins.};$$
$$10 \text{ ins.} = 20 \text{ half-ins.};$$

so $\qquad 7\frac{1}{2}$ ins. $= \dfrac{15}{20}$ of 10 ins. (Now, cancel by 5)

$$= \frac{3}{4} \text{ of 10 ins.}$$

(b) What fraction of 2 ft. is 1 ft. 3 ins.? Turn both measurements into inches.

$$1 \text{ ft. } 3 \text{ ins.} = 15 \text{ ins.};$$
$$2 \text{ ft.} \qquad = 24 \text{ ins.}$$

Therefore,

$$1 \text{ ft. } 3 \text{ ins.} = \frac{15}{24} \text{ of 2 ft.} \quad \text{(Now, cancel by 3)}$$

$$= \frac{5}{8} \text{ of 2 ft.}$$

EXERCISE III

In the same way that examples (a) and (b), above, were done, work the following:

1. What fraction of 6 ins. is 4 ins.?

2. What fraction of $7\frac{1}{2}$ ins. is $2\frac{1}{2}$ ins.?

3. What fraction of 12 ins. is 8 ins.?

4. What fraction of $11\frac{1}{4}$ ins. is $3\frac{3}{4}$ ins.?

5. What fraction of 15 ins. is $11\frac{1}{4}$ ins.?

6. What fraction of 2 ft. 3 ins. is 1 ft. 6 ins.?

7. What fraction of 3 ft. 9 ins. is 2 ft. 1 in.?

8. What fraction of 1 ft. 6 ins. is 1 ft.?

9. What fraction of 4 ft. 6 ins. is 2 ft. 6 ins.?

10. What fraction of 5 ft. 3 ins. is 1 ft. 9 ins.?

11. What fraction of $1\frac{1}{4}$ yds. is 1 ft. 3 ins.?

12. What fraction of $1\frac{1}{4}$ yds. is 1 yd.?

13. What fraction of 4 yds. is $1\frac{1}{4}$ yds.?

14. What fraction of $6\frac{1}{4}$ yds. is 5 yds.?

15. What fraction of $3\frac{3}{4}$ yds. is $2\frac{1}{4}$ yds.?

16. An upholsterer took $8\frac{1}{4}$ yds. of tapestry with him to re-cover a sofa. When he had finished he had $\frac{3}{4}$ of a yard left. What fraction of the complete length did he use?

17. A gate post 7 ft. long was sunk into the ground to a depth of 1 ft. 9 ins. What fraction of the post remained out of the ground?

18. A stretch of uneven road measuring 75 yds. was to be repaired. At the end of a week 48 yds. of it were completed. What fraction of the whole work was done during that week? What fraction remained to be repaired?

19. Half-a-cupful of water was added to four-and-a-half cupfuls of milk. The whole was then divided equally among five persons. What fraction of a cupful of milk did each person receive?

20. A motorist set out on a journey of 180 miles. By lunch time he had travelled 135 miles. What fraction of the journey had he still to do?

It is often necessary to be able to calculate the original width of some curtain material which has been draped, or to calculate the width of material which when draped will cover a given width.

Look at the diagram on page 8 where the draped width and the original width of some material are shown against the edge of a ruler. We see that the original width of the material is, as we say in ordinary speech, " half-as-wide-again " as the draped width; that is,

the original width $=1\frac{1}{2}$ times the draped width.

This may be written,

the original width $=\frac{3}{2}$ of the draped width,

because $\frac{3}{2}$ is only another way of writing $1\frac{1}{2}$.

It is interesting to compare the two statements, or *equations*, as we sometimes call them, between the draped width of some material and the original width:

First: The draped width $=\frac{2}{3}$ of the original width;

Second: The original width $=\frac{3}{2}$ of the draped width.

You should notice, if you have not already done so, that the fraction $\frac{3}{2}$ on the right-hand side of the second equation is the *inverse* of the fraction $\frac{2}{3}$ on the right-hand side of the first equation.

If the material is not wide enough to allow the draped width to be two-thirds of the original width, another fraction is chosen. For instance:

A piece of material, originally 5 ins. wide, is gathered to $3\frac{3}{4}$ ins. What fraction of the original width is the draped width, and *vice versa*? Again, a ruler will help us.

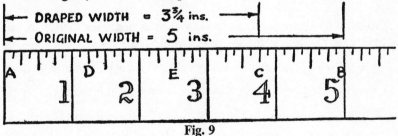

Fig. 9

AB represents the original width of the material.

AC represents the draped width.

The points D and E divide the draped width into three equal parts, each of which is $1\frac{1}{4}$ ins. long;

The points D, E and C divide the original width into four equal parts, each $1\frac{1}{4}$ ins. long;

so,   the draped width $=\frac{3}{4}$ of the original width;

and,   the original width $=\frac{4}{3}$ of the draped width.

Again we see that the fraction, $\frac{4}{3}$, on the right-hand side of the second equation is the inverse of the fraction, $\frac{3}{4}$, on the right-hand side of the first equation.

Now comes the question, " How shall we calculate a given fractional part of a given width of material? "

For instance, " What is two-thirds of 40 ins.? "

We can do this in several ways, of which the following two ways are most easily understood.

First, find one-third of 40 ins., that is, divide 40 ins. by three, and then double the answer and we shall have two-thirds of 40 ins.

$$\text{Working}$$

One-third of 40 ins. $= 13\frac{1}{3}$ ins. $\qquad 13\frac{1}{3} \times 2 = 26\frac{2}{3}$ ins.

so   two-thirds of 40 ins. $= 26\frac{2}{3}$ ins. $3\overline{)40 \text{ ins.}}$

Secondly, we find one-third of 40 ins. and then subtract it from 40 ins. (Why?)

One-third of 40 ins. $= \quad 13\frac{1}{3}$ ins.

so   two-thirds of 40 ins. $= \quad 40 \quad$ ins.

$$- 13\frac{1}{3} \text{ ins.}$$

$$= \quad 26\frac{2}{3} \text{ ins.}$$

Sometimes the second method is shorter than the first; in the above case, the first method is to be preferred.

When the fraction involved is greater than a whole one, say, $\frac{3}{2}$, or $\frac{4}{3}$, we use the second method, adding instead of subtracting.

What is $\frac{3}{2}$ of 28 ins.? (That is, what is $1\frac{1}{2}$ times 28 ins.?)

One-half of 28 ins. $= \quad 14$ ins.

therefore, $1\frac{1}{2}$ times 28 ins. $= \quad 28$ ins.

$$+ 14 \text{ ins.}$$

$$= \quad 42 \text{ ins.}$$

What is $\frac{4}{3}$ of 36 ins.? (That is, what is $1\frac{1}{3}$ times 36 ins.?)

One-third of 36 ins. $= \quad 12$ ins.

therefore, $1\frac{1}{3}$ times 36 ins. $= \quad 36$ ins.

$$+ 12 \text{ ins.}$$

$$= \quad 48 \text{ ins.}$$

EXERCISE IV

What is the draped width of each of the materials in Questions 1 and 2 if the draped width $=\frac{2}{3}$ of the original width?

1. Casement curtain material, 50 ins. wide?
   54 ins. wide?
   28 ins. wide?

2. Figured tapestry, 33 ins. wide?
   $1\frac{1}{2}$ yds. wide?
   52 ins. wide?

Using the same proportion for draping as in Questions 1 and 2, calculate the width of material needed to drape window or other openings of the widths in Questions 3 to 6 inclusive.

3. (a) 26 ins. (b) 30 ins.

4. (a) 1 ft. 4 ins. (b) 2 ft. 2 ins.

5. (a) Three-quarters of a yard. (b) A yard-and-a-quarter.

6. (a) Two-thirds of a yard. (b) A yard-and-one-third.

Calculate the draped width of the materials in Questions 7 and 8 if the draped width $=\frac{3}{4}$ of the original width.

7. Rayon rep material, 48 ins. wide;
   36 ins. wide;
   60 ins. wide.

8. Washable chintz, 33 ins. wide;
   $1\frac{1}{4}$ yds. wide;
   58 ins. wide.

Using the same proportion for draping, as in Questions 7 and 8, calculate the widths of materials needed to drape the window or other openings of the widths in Questions 9 to 12 inclusive.

9. (a) 42 ins. (b) 36 ins.

10. (a) 1 ft. 10 ins. (b) 2 ft. 9 ins.

11. (a) 1 yd. 1 ft. (b) One-half a yard.

12. (a) 2 ft. 3 ins. (b) Two-thirds of a yard.

13. A strip of chintz was folded backwards and forwards as shown below into three pleats, each 4 ins. wide; the over-laps are $1\frac{1}{2}$ ins.

Calculate (a) the pleated-length;
   (b) the total length of the material before pleating;
   (c) the pleated-length expressed as a fraction of the total length.

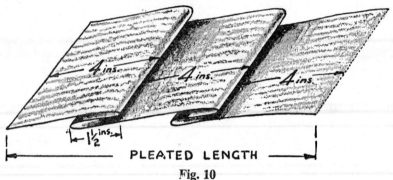

PLEATED LENGTH

Fig. 10

14. Calculate the total length of material to make three 4-in. pleats if the overlaps are $1\frac{3}{4}$ ins.

15. A piece of material 20 ins. long is to be folded to make 3 pleats, each 4 ins. wide. How much will the overlaps be?

16. What length of material would be needed to make 16 pleats like those in Question 13?

17. A piece of material four and one-third yds. long is to be folded into 20 pleats, each 4 ins. wide. Calculate the number of overlaps, and the size of each.

18. Calculate the pleated-length in Question 17, and express it as a fraction of the total length of the material.

19. When pleated into 5-in. pleats, a piece of material is to cover a length of $3\frac{1}{3}$ yds. Calculate the length of material needed if the overlaps are to be $1\frac{1}{4}$ ins.

20. A piece of material 4 yds. long is to be pleated to cover a length of $2\frac{1}{2}$ yds., the pleats to be not more than 4 ins. wide.

Calculate (a) the least number of pleats that may be made;
   (b) the width of that number of pleats;
   (c) the size of the overlaps.

The simplest way of gathering curtains and other hanging fabrics is to use rufflette tape. This can be bought quite cheaply at drapers' and ironmongers' shops. It is usually about three-quarters of an inch wide and contains two rows of thin string or twine which pass through slots in the tape.

Here is a sketch of a piece of rufflette tape before it is sewn on to the curtain.

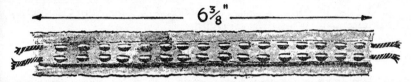

$6\frac{3}{8}$"

Fig. 11

What length would this rufflette tape appear when the curtain is gathered to two-thirds of its original width?

?

Fig. 12

We are to fit half-a-dozen curtains with rufflette tape, each curtain to be 2 ft. 3 ins. wide when gathered to two-thirds of its original width. How much tape, to the nearest half-yard, should we need?

Original width of each curtain $=\frac{3}{2}$ of the draped width;

$$= 1\frac{1}{2} \text{ times 2 ft. 3 ins.;}$$
$$= \quad 2 \text{ ft. 3 ins.}$$
$$\underline{+1 \text{ ft. } 1\frac{1}{2} \text{ ins.}}$$
$$= \quad 3 \text{ ft. } 4\frac{1}{2} \text{ ins.}$$
$$= 1 \text{ yd. and } \frac{1}{8} \text{ of a yd.}$$
$$= 1\frac{1}{8} \text{ yds.}$$

Length of tape for each curtain $= 1\frac{1}{8}$ yds.

Length of tape for six curtains $= 1\frac{1}{8}$ yds. $\times 6$
$$= 6\frac{6}{8} \text{ yds.}$$
$$= 6\frac{3}{4} \text{ yds.}$$

It would be necessary, therefore, to buy 7 yds. of rufflette tape.

EXERCISE V

Calculate the lengths of rufflette tape needed for the following:

1. 4 curtains for openings 1 ft. 6 ins. wide; gathering two-thirds of the original width.

2. 6 curtains for openings 1 ft. 9 ins. wide; gathering three-quarters of the original width.

3. A pair of hangings for an opening 3 ft. 9 ins. wide; gathering two-thirds of the original width.

4. A pair of curtains for an opening 2 ft. 6 ins. wide; gathering three-quarters of the original width.

5. A pair of curtains for an alcove 3 ft. 4 ins. wide; gathering two-thirds of the original width.

6. Here are dimensioned sketches of a sofa and easy chair which are to be fitted with loose-covers. Calculate the length in yds. of material, 8 ins. wide, needed to make the gathered frills round the bottoms of the covers, the gathered length being two-thirds of the original length of the material.

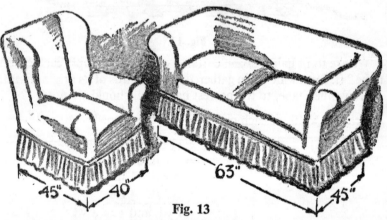

Fig. 13

7. The material for the frills in Question 6 is to be cut in lengths of 2 yds. from material 72 ins. wide. How many yds. of this material will be needed?

8. The waist-width of a gathered skirt is to be 28 ins. The gathered width is to be three-quarters of the original width. Calculate the waist-width before gathering.

This sketch shows how the hooks are inserted, about 4 ins. apart, into the rufflette tape.

Fig. 14

To find the correct spacing of the hooks for a given width of curtain, this is how we proceed: suppose the curtain were to be made from material originally 54 ins. wide.

We first see how many times, approximately, 4 ins. is contained in the whole width of the curtain. In this case by dividing 4 ins. into 54 ins. we find the answer lies between 13 and 14 as shown below:

$$\overline{\phantom{4 \text{ ins.}}} \; 13 + \text{times}$$

4 ins. $\overline{\big)\; 54 \text{ ins.}}$

        2 ins. remainder.

Therefore, if we divide the width of the curtain into 13 parts, each of the parts will be rather more than 4 ins.; if we divide it into 14 parts each of the parts will be less than 4 ins. Let us agree on 13 spaces. We now calculate the approximate distance between consecutive hooks.

     4 ins. and a little over one-eighth of an inch.

13 $\overline{\big)\; 54 \text{ ins.}}$

     2 ins. remainder

= 16 eighths of an inch remainder.

Therefore,

     distance between consecutive hooks = $4\frac{1}{8}$ ins. approximately.

How many hooks will be needed?

Look at the following sketch.

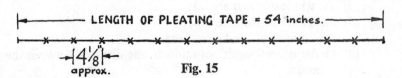

Fig. 15

The width of the curtain is divided into 13 equal parts by the 12 small crosses (×). A hook is to be placed at each of these points, and one at each end of the tape, making 14 hooks altogether.

It will be seen that the number of hooks is *one greater than the number of spaces* into which the curtain is to be divided.

EXERCISE VI

In all the following examples in which it is needed, assume that the gathered width of the material is two-thirds the original width, and that hooks should be about 4 ins. apart.

How many hooks would be needed for gathering tapes of the following lengths:

1. $1\frac{1}{4}$ yds.   **2.** 2 yds.   **3.** $1\frac{3}{4}$ yds.   **4.** $2\frac{1}{2}$ yds.

5. Calculate the number of hooks required for hanging a curtain, the ungathered width of which is 36 ins. How far apart—to the nearest eighth-of-an-inch—should the hooks be fixed in the rufflette tape ?

Fig. 16

6. This window is to be fitted with a pair of curtains. Calculate,
   (*a*) the width of the material;
   (*b*) the length of rufflette tape;
   (*c*) the number of hooks required;
   (*d*) to the nearest eighth-of-an-inch, the distance between the hooks.

7. How many hooks would be needed for a hanging for an alcove, 3 ft. 9 ins. wide? Calculate, to the nearest eighth of an inch, the distance between the hooks.

8. A pair of curtains is to cover a window opening 3 ft. 4 ins. wide, and to overlap 3 ins. in the middle. Calculate the width of the material required; the length of rufflette tape; the number of hooks, and their distance apart, to the nearest eighth-of-an-inch.

Fig. 17 shows how the curtain-rod should be fixed to the window frame by means of screws, and how the runners, to which the curtain is attached by means of the hooks, roll on the rod. The length of the rod should be equal to the overall width of the window including the moulding.

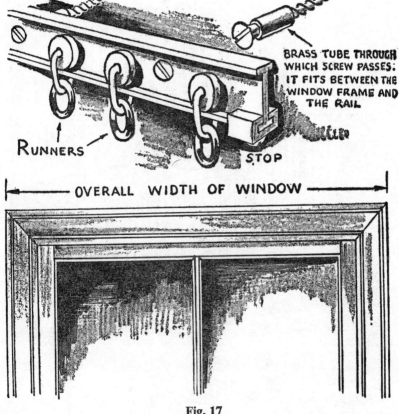

BRASS TUBE THROUGH WHICH SCREW PASSES: IT FITS BETWEEN THE WINDOW FRAME AND THE RAIL

RUNNERS

STOP

OVERALL WIDTH OF WINDOW

Fig. 17

c

D.L.M.

Now let us see what materials would be needed to make and fit a pair of curtains for the window shown in the picture opposite.

The overall width of the window is 5 ft. 4 ins.; the height of the window is 4 ft. 3 ins.

(*a*) Find the width of the material required.

The total width of the window = 5 ft. 4 ins.
Each curtain must, when draped, cover $\frac{1}{2}$ of 5 ft. 4 ins.
= 2 ft. 8 ins.
Width of each curtain before gathering = 2 ft. 8 ins. × $1\frac{1}{2}$
= 2 ft. 8 ins.
+1 ft. 4 ins.
= 4 ft.

Therefore, material 48 ins. wide would be needed.

(*b*) Find the total length of curtain material needed.

Note. Allow for hems, 1 in. at the top, and 2 ins. at the bottom. These should be added to the total height of the window to get the length of each curtain.

Total height of the window = 4 ft. 3 ins.
Allowance for hems = 3 ins.
Therefore, length of material for each curtain = 4 ft. 6 ins.
= $1\frac{1}{2}$ yds.

Therefore, total length of material needed for a pair of curtains
= 3 yds.

(*c*) Find the length of rufflette tape needed.

The width of the curtain material should be 4 ft.
Therefore, 8 ft., that is, $2\frac{2}{3}$ yds., of rufflette tape would be needed.

(*d*) Find the number of hooks needed.

If the hooks are to be about 4 ins. apart (before the material is pleated), we divide 48 ins. by 4 ins. This gives 12 spaces; so we need 13 hooks for each curtain.

The total number of hooks needed is 26; that is, 2 dozen and 2 hooks.

(*e*) Find the length of the curtain rod.

The overall width of the window is 5 ft. 4 ins., that is, $5\frac{1}{3}$ ft.

(*f*) Find the number of runners and end-stops needed.

12 runners and 1 end-stop would be needed for each curtain; that is, 2 dozen runners and 2 end-stops altogether.

(*g*) Find the total cost of all these materials using the prices given in the following list.

	WIDTH				
	28 ins.	36 ins.	42 ins.	48 ins.	54 ins.
CASEMENT CURTAIN CLOTH (per yd.)	4s.6d.	6s.	6s.6d.	7s.	7s.6d.
PLEATING TAPE (per yard)	6d.				

CURTAIN ROD 5½d. per foot	HOOKS 1s.3d. per dozen.	RUNNERS 1s.9d. per dozen.	END·STOPS 1s.6d. per dozen.

EXERCISE VII

In each of the questions below, calculate in seven stages, as we did on pages 21 and 22, the quantities of materials, of widths given in the price-list above, needed to make and fix pairs of curtains to windows of the sizes given; allow gathering fraction, two-thirds approximately.

1. Overall width 4 ft.; height 5 ft. 3 ins.

2. Overall width 6 ft.; height 3 ft. 9 ins.

3. Overall width 4 ft. 6 ins.; height 6 ft. 9 ins.

4. Overall width 3 ft. 6 ins.; height 5 ft. 6 ins.

5. Overall width 2 ft. 4 ins.; height 3 ft. 6 ins.

6. Overall width 5 ft. 3 ins.; height 7 ft. 6 ins.

7. Overall width 5 ft. 9 ins.; height 8 ft. 6 ins.

8. Overall width 4 ft. 8 ins.; height 6 ft. 3 ins.

9. Overall width 3 ft. 6 ins.; height 6 ft. 6 ins.

10. You are to make a pair of hangings for the dressing-stand shown under the window in the bedroom in the picture on page 20.

> The stand is 2 ft. 9 ins. high;
> it projects 1 ft. 6 ins. from the wall;
> its width is 5 ft. 4 ins. (the same as the window).

Allowing 1 in. for hem at the top, and 2 ins. for hem at the bottom, and the gathering to be in the same proportion as in the curtains, calculate the length and width of each hanging, and the amount of rufflette tape needed.

II

WORKSHOP DRAWING

Freehand sketches and measured drawings

Before you start this section you should refresh your memory about addition and subtraction of such fractions as are to be found on a carpenter's rule; halves, quarters, eighths and sixteenths of an inch. (See pages 252–257.)

Measuring halves and quarters

Fig. 1 is a drawing of a rectangular piece of wood from which two rectangular pieces have been removed. On the drawing you see some faint lines, eight of which, called *dimension-lines*, have arrow points at each end. One of these dimension-lines reaches from end to end of the piece of wood; another marks the width; others indicate important measurements of other parts of it.

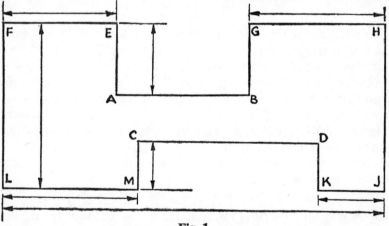

Fig. 1

Suppose you were asked to make, in the school workshop, a piece of wood or a piece of tinplate the same size and shape as that shown in the drawing above. You would naturally, first of all, measure the length and breadth of the material with either a two-foot rule, or an ordinary twelve-inch rule.

You will find that the length is $4\frac{1}{4}$ ins.: the breadth $1\frac{3}{4}$ ins. Therefore you will need a piece of wood or tinplate

$$4\frac{1}{4} \text{ ins. by } 1\frac{3}{4} \text{ ins.,}$$

or written more briefly,

$$4\frac{1}{4}'' \times 1\frac{3}{4}''.$$

In such expressions the so-called multiplication sign, $\times$, is to be read as the word *by*, not as *times*.

(You will often meet such expressions. For instance, the size of a drawing-board may be written: 30 ins. $\times$ 22 ins.; or the size of a photograph: $3\frac{1}{4}'' \times 2\frac{1}{4}''$.)

The remaining six dimension-lines in the figure on page 25 are sufficient to help you to find the sizes of the two rectangles that have to be removed, and their positions.

What are the dimensions of the rectangle *EABG*?

Measure the dimension-line near *EA*. You will find that it is $\frac{3}{4}$ in. long. That is the breadth of the rectangle.

Its length may be calculated from the measurements *FE* and *GH*, as follows:

By direct measurement, $FE = 1\frac{1}{4}$ ins.
$GH = 1\frac{1}{2}$ ins.

Add these two dimensions together, and subtract their sum from the total length of the piece of material and you will have the length of the piece that has to be removed.

Now, a joiner, or a mechanic, would do these calculations " in his head ", that is, mentally, so we shall follow his example.

Adding together $1\frac{1}{4}$ ins. and $1\frac{1}{2}$ ins. we get $2\frac{3}{4}$ ins., which when taken away from the total length, namely, $4\frac{1}{4}$ ins., leaves $1\frac{1}{2}$ ins. This should now be checked by direct measurement.

Thus the size of the rectangle to be removed from the upper part of the material is

$$1\frac{1}{2}'' \times \frac{3}{4}'',$$

and the end *EA* must be $1\frac{1}{4}$ ins. from the end *LF* of the material; the end *BG* will then be $1\frac{1}{2}$ ins. from *HJ*.

In the same way you can find the length and breadth of the rectangle *CMKD*.

By direct measurement, $CM = \frac{1}{2}$ in.

The length *CD* is obtained by subtracting the sum of the lengths of *LM* and *KJ* from $4\frac{1}{4}$ ins.

By direct measurement, $LM = 1\frac{1}{2}$ ins.

$$KJ = \frac{3}{4} \text{ in.}$$

The sum of LM and KJ $= 2\frac{1}{4}$ ins.

Therefore the length of the rectangle $CMKD$ is 2 ins. This should be checked by direct measurement.

Therefore the size of the rectangle to be removed from the lower part of the material is $2'' \times \frac{1}{2}''$.

A craftsmen is often asked to make an exact copy of something. If he cannot keep the original until he has made the copy, he will probably make a freehand sketch of the original, and on it insert all the necessary measurements. Such a sketch is called a *freehand dimensioned sketch*.

A draughtsman may be asked to make workshop drawings of a defective part of a machine. He, too, would " measure it up ", to use the workshop phrase, and make a freehand dimensioned sketch from which he would then prepare the workshop drawings or blueprints for the guidance of the workman who is to carry out the repairs.

In this chapter, you will get plenty of practice in making freehand sketches from actual objects, and in making measured drawings with ruler and set-squares from them. In preparation for this work, here is some advice on the use of ruler and set-squares.

Suppose you wish to draw a line joining two points A and B.

First place the point of your pencil at the point B and slide the upper edge of the ruler up to it. Then rotate the ruler until the upper edge passes through the point A. The ruler is then in the correct position for the drawing of the line.

Press the ruler tightly to the paper with thumb and fingers on the left hand, and draw the line along the upper edge from left to right as shown by the arrow in Fig. 2.

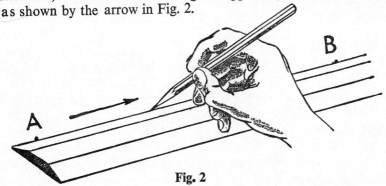

Fig. 2

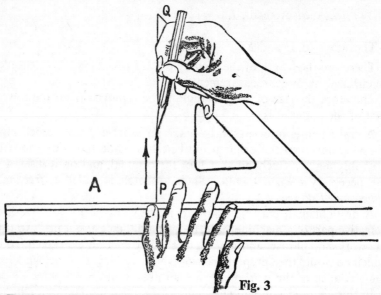

Fig. 3

To draw a line at right angles to the ruler at, say, the point A, lay the set-square along the uppermost edge of the ruler and place the point of the pencil at A; slide the set-square along the edge of the ruler until the edge PQ of the set-square touches the pencil, then draw the line along that edge, *in the direction away from the ruler,* that is, from P to Q as shown in Fig. 3.

Imagine Fig 1 on page 25 to be a shaped block of wood, and that you are to make a freehand dimensioned sketch of it, and from this, a neat measured workshop drawing.

You will need a drawing-book, with pages about 12 ins. × 9 ins.

In the top right-hand corner of a page make a freehand dimensioned sketch as shown in Fig. 4: this will occupy a space about $4\frac{1}{2}$ ins. × $2\frac{3}{4}$ ins. ($PQRS$).

The measured drawing should be arranged as near as possible to the centre of the rest of the page. In order to do this some simple mental calculations are necessary.

The distance from the line QR to the bottom of the page is $2\frac{3}{4}$ ins. less than the width of the page, that is, $2\frac{3}{4}$ ins. less than 9 ins.; which is $6\frac{1}{4}$ ins. Now, since the breadth of the block of wood is $1\frac{3}{4}$ ins., take $1\frac{3}{4}$ ins. from $6\frac{1}{4}$ ins., and divide the remainder into two equal parts: each part will be $2\frac{1}{4}$ ins., so draw the line YX parallel to the bottom of the page, and $2\frac{1}{4}$ ins. from it.

Next draw a line parallel to this, $1\frac{3}{4}$ ins.—that is the width of the block of wood—from *YX*.

The length of the page is 12 ins., and that of the block of wood $4\frac{1}{4}$ ins.; so if you subtract $4\frac{1}{4}$ ins. from 12 ins., and divide the remainder by two you will have the amount of space between the ends of the drawing of the block and the edges of the page.

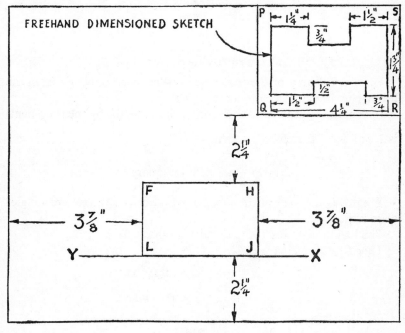

Fig. 4

$4\frac{1}{4}$ ins. from 12 ins. leaves $7\frac{3}{4}$ ins.; one-half of this is $3\frac{7}{8}$ ins.; draw, with faint lines, the rectangle *FLJH*, $4\frac{1}{4}$ ins. × $1\frac{3}{4}$ ins. as shown; the rectangle will then be well spaced on the page.

Complete the drawing from the measurements in the freehand dimensioned sketch. Rub out the faint lines *EG* and *MK*; line-in the rest, and print the dimensions on their corresponding dimension-lines.

Now refresh your memory about multiplication of fractions. (See pages 257–262.)

Referring to the rectangular piece of wood, figure on page 25, find the *area* of the rectangle that has been removed from the upper part.

We found by calculation that the length of this rectangle is $1\frac{1}{2}$ ins.; its breadth found by measurement is $\frac{3}{4}$ of an inch.

Therefore, the area $=1\frac{1}{2}$ ins. $\times \frac{3}{4}$ of an inch

$$=\frac{3}{2}\times\frac{3}{4} \ square \ \text{ins.}$$

$$=\frac{9}{8} \text{ square ins.}$$

$$=1\frac{1}{8} \text{ square ins.}$$

What is the area of the rectangle that has been removed from the lower part of the piece of wood?

Its length, by calculation, is 2 ins.; its breadth, by measurement, is $\frac{1}{2}$ an inch; therefore, its area is

$$2 \text{ ins.} \times \frac{1}{2} \text{ an inch} = 1 \text{ square in.}$$

What was the area of the piece of wood before the two rectangles were removed?

The length is $4\frac{1}{4}$ ins.; the breadth $1\frac{3}{4}$ ins.

Therefore, the area was $4\frac{1}{4}$ ins. $\times 1\frac{3}{4}$ ins;

$$=4\frac{1}{4}\times1\frac{3}{4} \text{ square ins.}$$

$$=\frac{17}{4}\times\frac{7}{4} \text{ square ins.}$$

$$=\frac{119}{16} \text{ square ins.}$$

$$=7\frac{7}{16} \text{ square ins.}$$

What is the area of the piece of wood left?

The total area before the pieces were removed was $7\frac{7}{16}$ square ins. The parts removed were $1\frac{1}{8}$ square ins. and 1 square in.; that is, $2\frac{1}{8}$ square ins.

We must now take $2\frac{1}{8}$ square ins. from $7\frac{7}{16}$ square ins.

We do this mentally, in two stages.

First, we take $\frac{1}{8}$ from $7\frac{7}{16}$; the remainder is $7\frac{5}{16}$.

Now we take away the 1 square in., and we have left $6\frac{5}{16}$ square ins.

EXERCISE VIII

Make a freehand dimensioned sketch and a neat measured drawing of each of the diagrams (Fig. 5 to Fig. 9). The measurements are in halves and quarters of an inch. Calculate the areas of the shaded portions of the drawings: *A, B, C*, etc.

1.

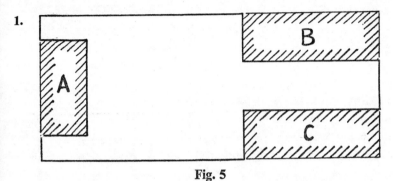

Fig. 5

2.

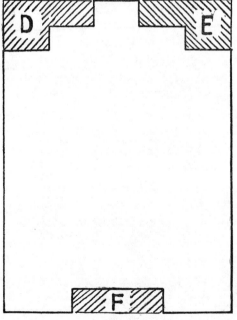

Fig. 6

3.

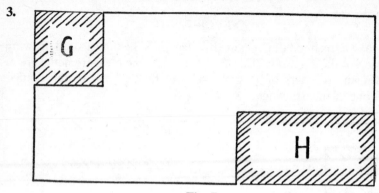

Fig. 7

4.

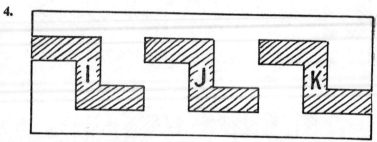

Fig. 8

5.

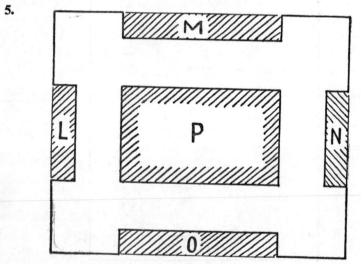

Fig. 9

EXERCISE IX

Make a freehand dimensioned sketch and a neat measured drawing of each of the diagrams (Fig. 10 to Fig. 18).   You will now be using eighths and sixteenths of an inch as well as halves and quarters of an inch.

1.

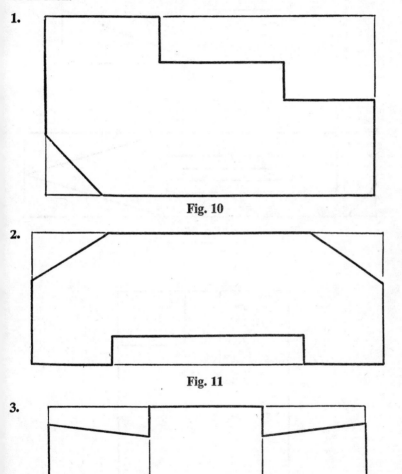

Fig. 10

2.

Fig. 11

3.

Fig. 12

4.

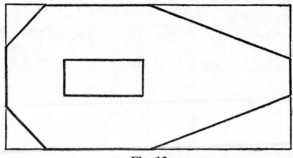

Fig. 13

5.

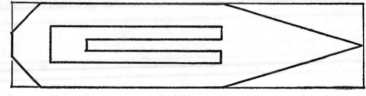

Fig. 14

6.

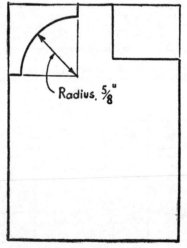

Fig. 15

7.

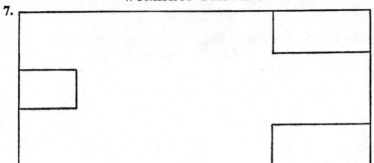

Fig. 16

8.

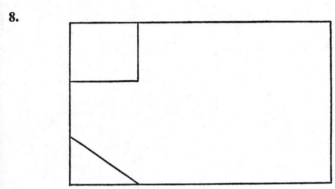

Fig. 17

9.

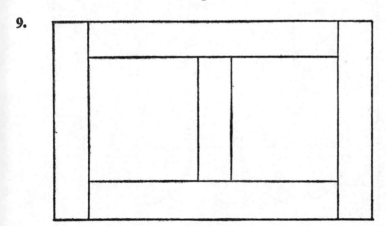

Fig. 18

EXERCISE X

Make a freehand sketch and a neat dimensioned drawing of each of the diagrams (Fig. 19 to Fig 22). You will now be using thirds, sixths and twelfths of an inch.

1.

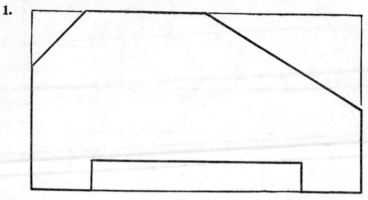

Fig. 19

2.

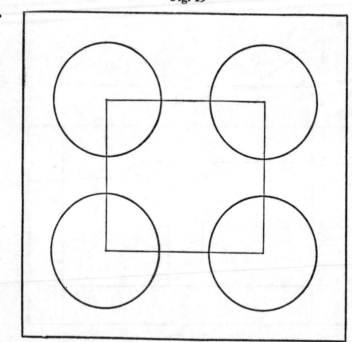

Fig. 20

3.

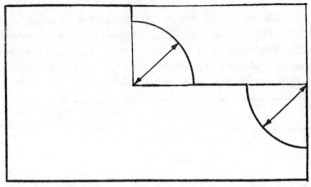

Fig. 21

4.

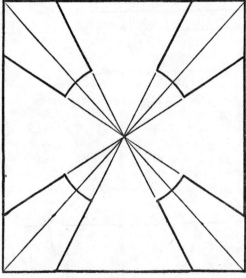

Fig. 22

EXERCISE XI

Make a freehand sketch and a neat measured drawing of each of the diagrams (Fig. 23 to Fig. 26). Express the measurements both as ordinary fractions and as decimals as shown in two of the dimensions in Question 1. Before you begin you should refresh your memory about decimals. (See pages 264–269.)

1.

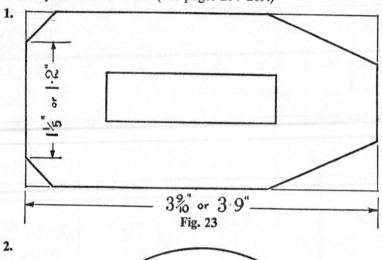

Fig. 23

2.

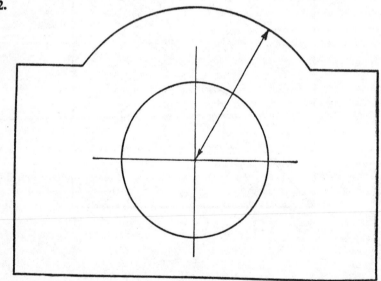

Fig. 24

3.

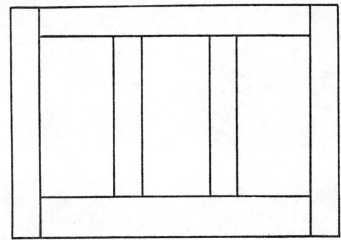

Fig. 25

4.

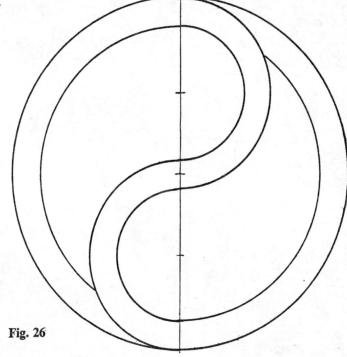

Fig. 26

III

SCALES AND MAP MEASUREMENTS

Hiking and cycling

Hiking and cycling are two popular, enjoyable, and inexpensive pastimes. If we wish to enjoy these pleasures to the full we should get accustomed to the use of maps of the localities we wish to explore. These can be bought, at reasonable cost, at most booksellers.

What kind of maps should we use?

For hiking purposes, since the distances to be covered are not very great, we need a fairly large scale map. The best are probably the Ordnance Survey, one-mile-to-the-inch, and two-miles-to-the-inch, maps. These are in sheets measuring about 2 ft. 3 ins. by 1 ft. 6 ins., and show main roads and country-roads; field paths; railways; rivers and streams; " contours "; woods, and so on. On the next page is a sketch from part of a " 2-miles-to-the-inch " Bartholomew's Coloured Contour Map covering the district around Sevenoaks in Kent.

Suppose you are camping near Wrotham, and you decide on an afternoon's tramp westward along the Pilgrims Way, returning through Kemsing, Noah's Ark, and Fuller Street, then eastward passing the Roman Camp at Oldbury Hill, through Ightham to Borough Green, and finally northward back to Wrotham. It would be well, before setting out, to make an estimate of the number of miles in this circular tour, To do this, lay a piece of cotton or very thin string along the route, and then measure its length. The length in half-inches is the length of the journey in miles. Allowing for half-an-hour's rest near the Roman Camp, and for walking at the rate of $2\frac{1}{2}$ miles an hour, how long would this journey take?

EXERCISE XII

The following routes are to be traced from the two-miles-to-the-inch map on page 42.

1. Make a tracing of the route from Wrotham, along the Pilgrims Way, Kemsing, Fuller Street, Oldbury Hill, Ightham, Borough Green to Wrotham.

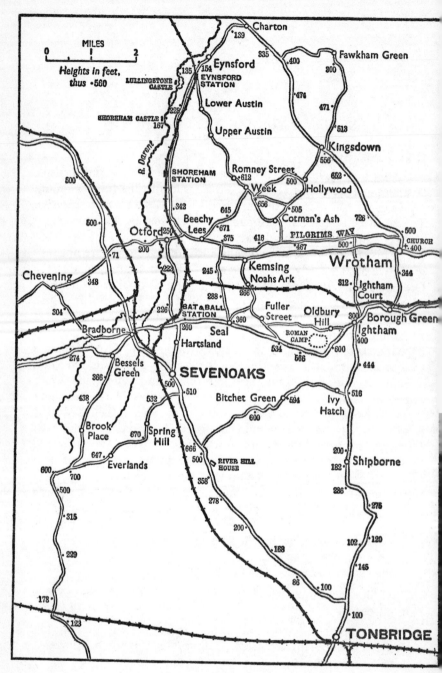

Make tracings of each of the following routes, and estimate their respective lengths to the nearest mile:

2. Sevenoaks,
   Bradbourne,
   Chevening,
   Otford,
   Bat and Ball Station,
   Hartsland,
   Sevenoaks.

3. Sevenoaks,
   Bradbourne,
   Bessels Green,
   Brook Place,
   Everlands,
   Spring Hill,
   Sevenoaks.

4. Tonbridge,
   Shipborne,
   Ivy Hatch,
   Bitchet Green,
   Riverhill House,
     and by the main road to
   Tonbridge.

5. Wrotham, north to
   Pilgrims Way,
   Cotman's Ash,
   Week,
   Romney Street,
   Upper and Lower Austin,
   Eynsford Station,
   Shoreham Station,
   Beechy Lees,
   Pilgrims Way to Wrotham.

6. Eynsford,
   Charton,
   Fawkham Green,
   Kingsdown,
   Week,
   Eynsford.

7. Sevenoaks,
   Otford,
   Eynsford,
   Wrotham,
   Ightham,
   Shipborne,
   Tonbridge,
   Sevenoaks.

Road gradients

It is interesting to know, before one sets out on either a walking-tour or a cycle-run, whether the roads are level or hilly, and if hilly, whether the hills are gentle slopes or steep. These things we can usually find out from maps.

Let us look again at the " Two-miles-to-the-inch " map opposite.

The valley of the river Darent runs almost due north and south. Near Otford, the Pilgrims Way crosses the river. Near the river, on the west bank, we see the number 200. What does this mean?

It means that the land at that point is 200 feet above sea-level.

Near Shoreham Castle it is 167 feet above sea-level, and a little to the north of Lullingstone Castle, 135 feet above.

Therefore, we conclude that the land slopes downwards from Otford to Lullingstone Castle, therefore the river flows from south to north.

Now let us examine the gradients of the road from Wrotham to Kingsdown.

Near the church at Wrotham the road is 400 feet above sea-level. About half-a-mile north it rises to 500 feet; three-quarters of a mile further it attains its greatest height, namely, 726 feet above sea-level. It then descends to 652 feet near Hollywood, and to 566 feet before reaching Kingsdown.

Thus, during the first half-mile from Wrotham the road rises 100 feet; during the next three-quarters of a mile it rises 226 feet. Therefore the gradient immediately on leaving Wrotham is not quite so steep as that up to the highest point.

Now, from the highest point to Hollywood—a distance of about a mile—the road descends to 652 feet above sea-level, that is, 74 feet, and during the next three-quarters of a mile it descends a further 86 feet. Therefore the downward gradient from the highest point to Hollywood is less steep than that from Hollywood to Kingsdown.

We can represent these gradients on squared paper, and so we can compare them.

We shall choose the following scales:

   Distances along the road: Half-a-mile-to-the-inch.
   Heights above sea-level: One inch represents 500 feet.

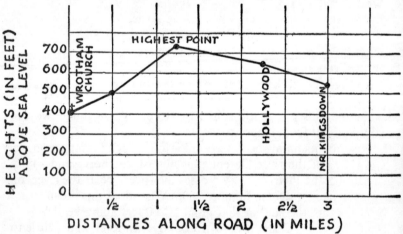

Fig. 1

The diagram, which is called a " section ", does not show the actual slopes because the vertical scale is not the same as the horizontal scale, but it does show how the slopes vary between the places selected.

EXERCISE XIII

When necessary, in the following examples, refer to the " two-miles-to-the-inch " map on page 42.

1. The road about 1 mile west of Wrotham runs almost due south from a point on the Pilgrims Way, 500 feet above sea-level, to Ightham, 300 feet above sea-level. Near Ightham Court it is 312 feet above sea-level.
Measure the distances from the Pilgrims Way to Ightham Court, and from Ightham Court to Ightham, and draw a section, to the scales: ½ mile to the inch, and 250 ft. to the inch.

2. Take the necessary data from the map for the road running northward from Seal across the valley about three-quarters of a mile west of Kemsing, to a point on the Pilgrims Way near Beechy Lees, and then draw a section of the road to the same scales as in Question 1.
Draw a section along the road from Ightham to Shipborne to the same scales as Question 1.

4. Draw a section along the road from Otford to Sevenoaks.

5. Draw a section along the road shown below (Fig. 2) from *A* to *B*.

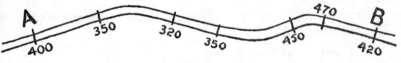

Fig. 2

More about road gradients

When studying the gradients on the road from Wrotham to Kingsdown on pages 42 and 44 we saw that during the first half-mile it ascended 100 feet (i.e. from 400 feet to 500 feet). During the next three-quarters of a mile it ascended 226 feet; then, in the next mile it descended 74 feet, and finally in the next three-quarters of a mile it descended 86 feet.

We cannot, at once, compare the gradients in the road from these particulars, but we could, of course, calculate them.

Road gradients are usually expressed in the following way:

"1 in 120"   or   "1 in 75".

The first expression means that the road rises 1 foot in a length along it of 120 feet.

The second road rises 1 foot in a length along it of 75 feet.

Expressed in this way it is easy to see which is the steeper gradient.

Let us compare the gradients "1 in 3" and "1 in 4". Draw the line BC, 1 in. long, at right-angles to AB (Fig. 3). With centre C, draw an arc of a circle 3 ins. radius, cutting AB at D. Join DC; this gives us a gradient of "1 in 3".

Now, with centre C, draw an arc of a circle 4 ins. radius, cutting AB at E. Join EC; this gives us a gradient of "1 in 4".

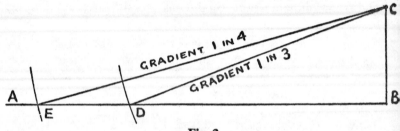

Fig. 3

Thus we see that a gradient of "1 in 3" is steeper than one of "1 in 4". Similarly, we see that a gradient of "1 in 75" is steeper than one of "1 in 120".

Let us now express the gradients of the road from Wrotham to Kingsdown in this way.

First portion, half-a-mile long.

Rise is	100 feet in ½ mile;
that is,	100 feet in 880 × 3 feet;
that is,	100 feet in 2640 feet;
that is,	1 in 26·4.

Second portion, three-quarters of a mile long.

Rise is	226 feet in ¾ of 5280 feet;
that is,	226 feet in 3960 feet;
that is,	1 in $\frac{3960}{226}$;

$$\begin{array}{r} 17\cdot5 \text{ approx.} \\ \hline 226\ )\ \overline{3960} \\ 226 \\ \hline 1700 \\ 1582 \\ \hline 1180 \\ 1130 \\ \hline \end{array}$$

Therefore, the gradient of the second portion is

1 in 17·5 approx.

Third portion, 1 mile—that is, 5280 feet—long.

Fall is   74 feet in 5280 feet;

that is,   1 foot in $\frac{5280}{74}$ feet,

therefore the gradient is

1 in 71 approx.

Fourth portion, three-quarters of a mile—that is, 3960 feet—long.

Fall is   86 feet in 3960 feet;

that is,   1 foot in $\frac{3960}{86}$ feet;

therefore, the gradient is

1 in 46 approx.

Thus, arranged in order of *decreasing* steepness, we have

Portion	Gradient
Second	1 in 17·5
First	1 in 26·4
Fourth	1 in 46
Third	1 in 71

Rail-track gradients

When constructing rail-tracks, railway engineers always try to choose routes that will, as far as possible, avoid hills with steep gradients, but they cannot avoid them altogether.

On the side of the rail-track, in order to help the engine-drivers, gradient-indicators are fixed at all points where the gradients change. You may have noticed them; they look like this:

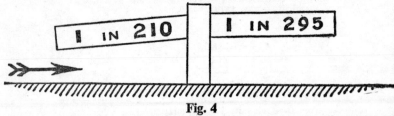

Fig. 4

When an engine-driver, travelling in the direction shown by the arrow, arrives at the point where the above sign or indicator is fixed, he knows that he must give the engine less steam because the incline on which he is entering is less steep than the one he is leaving: the former being 1 in 210, the latter 1 in 295.

A gradient-indicator like that below informs the driver that the track on the left is level, and that on the right is a descent of 1 in 198.

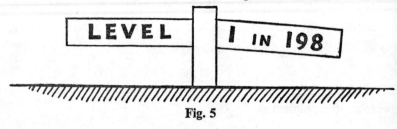

Fig. 5

EXERCISE XIV

Calculate the gradients in Questions 1 to 5.

1. A rise of 160 feet in three-quarters of a mile.
2. A rise of 220 feet in five furlongs.
3. A descent of 60 feet in three furlongs.
4. A descent of 127 feet in a mile-and-a-quarter.
5. A rise of 245 feet in a mile-and-a-half.
6. On a stretch of road three furlongs long the upward gradient is 1 in 125. Calculate the height, in feet, of the highest point on the road above the lowest.
7. From A a road descends for half-a-mile to B. The gradient is 1 in 63. Calculate the height of A above B.

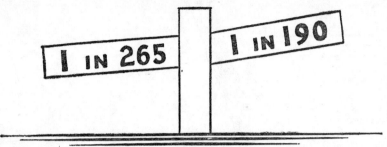

Fig. 6

8. This railway gradient-indicator is the junction of two gradients: that on the left, 420 yards long; that on the right, 500 yards long. How many feet upwards does a train climb in ascending these two portions of the track?

9. In the A.A. Road Handbook, about the road from Glastonbury to Ilfracombe, we read " the general gradient on Porlock Hill is 1—8 (this means 1 in 8) with maximum gradient in one part 1—4 ". If the steepest part is 300 yds. long, and the whole road up the hill $\frac{1}{2}$ a mile, calculate, in feet:

(*a*) the rise on the 1—4 stretch;
(*b*) the total rise on the whole hill.

10. On a 1-mile-to-the-inch Ordnance map, the distance along a road between the 50 ft. contour line and the 100 ft. contour line was three-quarters of an inch. Calculate the average gradient of that part of the road.

Cyclist's route charts

On the next page is a sketch (scale 2·5 miles-to-the-inch) reduced from a Bartholomew's Two-miles-to-the-inch Coloured Contour Map covering an interesting part of the Lake District including parts of Lake Windermere and Lake Coniston.

Newby Bridge, on the River Leven which flows out of Lake Windermere at the southern end, is a very good centre for exploring this part of the Lake District.

Let us prepare a Route Chart for a cycle-run from Newby Bridge to Ulverston (Fig. 7).

Trace, on tracing-paper, the route, and on it mark the places: Newby Bridge, Backbarrow, Haverthwaite, Greenodd, Ulverston.

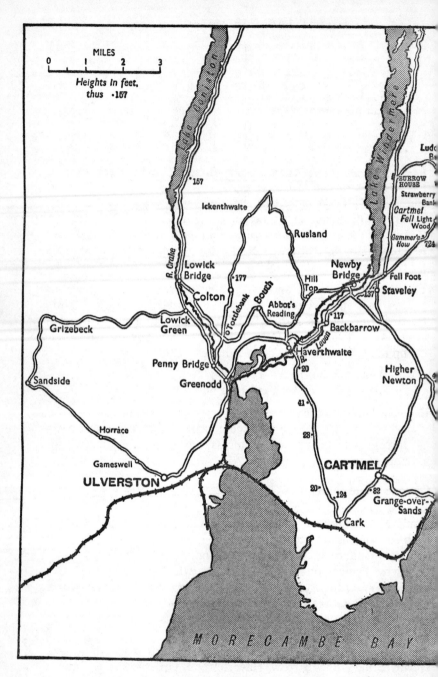

Estimate, or measure by means of string or cotton, the distance between Newby Bridge and Backbarrow; Backbarrow and Haverthwaite; and so on, and enter the whole of this information like this:

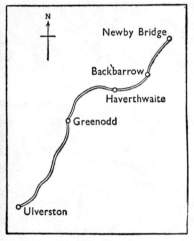

ROUTE CHART Newby Bridge to Ulverston	
Miles	
	Newby Bridge
1½	Backbarrow
1½	Haverthwaite
2	Greenodd
4	Ulverston
9	

Total miles = 9

Fig. 7

EXERCISE XV

Make out ROUTE CHARTS for each of the following cycle runs:

1. Newby Bridge,
Higher Newton,
Grange-over-Sands,
Cartmel,
Cark,
Haverthwaite,
Newby Bridge.

2. Newby Bridge,
Haverthwaite,
Greenodd,
Ulverston,
Gameswell,
Horrace,
Sandside,
Grizebeck,
Lowick Green,
Penny Bridge,
Greenodd,
Newby Bridge.

D.L.M.

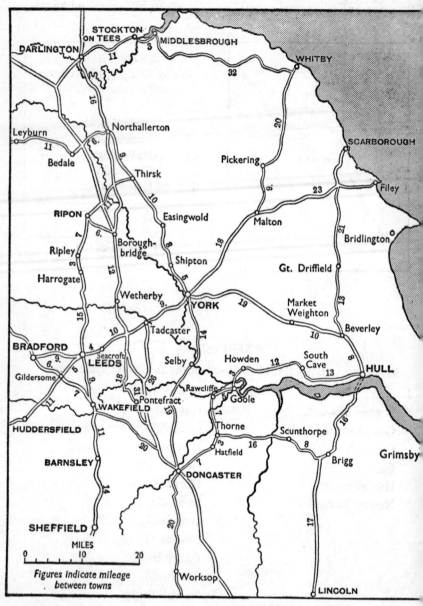

Figures indicate mileage between towns

3. Newby Bridge,
   Fell Foot,
   Light Wood (east of Cartmel
      Fell),
   Strawberry Bank,
   Ludder Burn,
   Burrow House,
      and by the main road east
      of Lake Windermere to
   Newby Bridge.
   N.B.—You will have to walk
      from Fell Foot to a point
      beyond Gummer's How
      Plantation because, as the
      map shows, the road rises
      from 137 feet above sea-
      level near Stavely to 724
      feet before it reaches Light
      Wood.   Calculate   the
      gradient of this part of the
      road.

4. Any route you consider suitable
   from Newby Bridge to Lake
   Coniston, returning by a different route.

5. Newby Bridge,
   Hill Top,
   Abbot's Reading,
   Bouth (pronounced Booth),
   Tottlebank,
   Colton,
   Ickenthwaite,
   Rusland,
   Hill Top,
   Newby Bridge.

Motorist's route charts

On the page opposite to this there is a part of a 16-miles-to-the-inch motoring-map covering the region round York.

On it you will find numbers which indicate the number of miles along the road from one small circle to the next.   By means of such maps, it is a very simple matter to prepare a Motorist's Route Chart for a journey.   For instance:

Prepare a Motorist's Route Chart between York and Leyburn.

Miles		Notes
	York	
5	Shipton	
8	Easingwold	
10	Thirsk	
9	Northallerton	←At Northallerton
6	Bedale	crossroads, turn
11	Leyburn	left for Bedale
Total 49		

To find the distance " as the crow flies ", that is, the distance by air between two towns, measure the distance on the map—in inches and sixteenths of an inch if the scale of the map is 16-miles-to-the-inch: calculation is then very simple.

For instance: How many miles is it " as the crow flies " from Doncaster to Hull?

The distance on the map is $2\frac{1}{4}$ ins.

Therefore, the distance in miles $= 16 \times 2\frac{1}{4}$ miles
$$= 32 + 4 \text{ miles}$$
$$= 36 \text{ miles.}$$

Let us compare this with the distance by road via Goole, Howden, and South Cave.

Miles		Notes
	Doncaster	
7	Hatfield	
3	Thorne	
7	Rawcliffe	
5	Goole	
3	Howden	
12	South Cave	
13	Hull	
Total 50		

Therefore, it is 14 miles further by road than by air.

EXERCISE XVI

Make out Route Charts for each of the following journeys:

1. York,
Tadcaster,
Seacroft,
Leeds,
Bradford.

2. Leeds,
York,
Market Weighton,
Beverley,
Hull.

3. Sheffield,
Barnsley,
Wakefield,
Gildersome,
Bradford.

4. Worksop,
Doncaster,
Pontefract,
Wetherby,
Ripon.

Find the distance " as the crow flies ", that is, in a straight line between the following pairs of towns:

5. Hull and Lincoln.

6. Sheffield and Grimsby.

7. Bradford and Scarborough.

8. Lincoln and York.

9. Selby and Whitby.

10. Bridlington and Middlesborough.

EXERCISE XVII

This is a map, drawn to a scale of " one-sixteenth of an inch to a mile ".

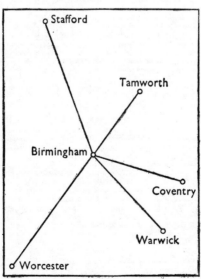

Fig. 8

1. By direct measurements from Fig. 8, find the following distances:

    (*a*) From Birmingham to Coventry;
    (*b*) From Birmingham to Tamworth;
    (*c*) From Birmingham to Stafford;
    (*d*) From Birmingham to Worcester;
    (*e*) From Birmingham to Warwick.

2. How many miles is it, as the crow flies, from Worcester to Stafford?

3. An airman started from Stafford and flew the following route: Tamworth, Coventry, Warwick, Worcester, and returned direct to Stafford. How many miles did he cover in the flight?

4. Draw a map, showing the same towns as in the one above, in which the scale shall be one-eighth of an inch to a mile.

EXERCISE XVIII

Here is a map of England and Wales. The scale is not given.

Fig. 9

1. Measure, to the nearest tenth of an inch, the distance on the map (Fig. 9) from Manchester to London.

2. The distance by air from Manchester to London is 175 miles. Calculate the approximate scale of the map in miles-to-the-inch.

Using the result of Question 2, find the distances by air between the towns in Questions 3 and 4.

3. London and Newcastle;   Hull and Cardiff;
   London and Holyhead;   Liverpool and Harwich;
   London and Plymouth;   Warwick and Cromer.

4. Manchester and Newcastle;   Liverpool and Cromer;
   Hull and Southampton;   Cambridge and Holyhead;
   Plymouth and Harwich;   Croydon and Newcastle.

5. Determine the length, in miles, of the following route:
   Liverpool; Manchester; Hull; Cromer; Harwich; Croydon; Liverpool.

6. An airman flew the following route:
   Croydon; Southampton; Bristol; Birmingham; Cambridge; Croydon.
   He started at 3.15 p.m., and returned at 5 p.m. Calculate the length of the journey, and his approximate speed in miles per hour.

IV

VOLUME, DENSITY AND CAPACITY

Volume

The volume of a thing—such as a tool-chest, a football, a lump of coal—is the measure of the space it occupies. The bigger a thing is, the more space it occupies. If we say " *this* box is bigger than *that* box ", we mean, " *this* box occupies more space than *that* box ". Let us now see how to measure the volume of an object. We shall start with rectangular objects.

We must have some kind of *unit* in which to express volumes. If the things are small we express their volumes in *cubic inches*; larger things, such as planks of timber, brick walls, and so on, are expressed in *cubic feet*; still larger things such as heaps of sand, quantity of earth in a trench, are expressed in *cubic yards*.

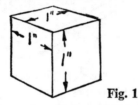

Fig. 1

A cube, edges 1 inch long, is called a *cubic inch* (Fig. 1).

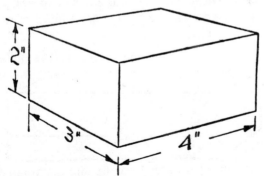

Fig. 2

How many cubic inches can you cut from a block of wood, 4 inches long, 3 inches broad, and 2 inches thick (Fig. 2)?

59

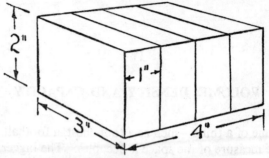

Fig. 3

First, mark out the block, using a ruler and try-square, into 4 slabs as shown in Fig. 3. Each of these slabs when cut will be 3 inches by 2 inches, 1 inch thick; as shown in Fig. 3.

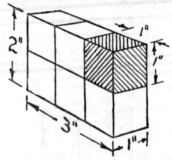

Fig. 4

Now mark out one of the slabs as shown in Fig. 4. It will be seen that you can cut 6 cubic inches from each slab; therefore from the whole block you can cut 24 cubic inches, so we say the volume of the block, 4 inches × 3 inches × 2 inches, is 24 cubic inches.

In the same way you will find that, from a block of wood

12 ins. × 4 ins. × 4 ins., (Fig. 5)

you could cut 12 times 16 cubic inches, that is, 192 cubic inches.

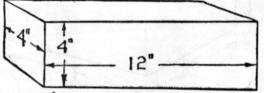

Fig. 5

Can you now make up a rule for finding the volume of a rectangular block of anything? If so, write it down at the back of your exercise book for future reference.

EXERCISE XIX

1. Calculate, in cubic inches, the volume of this match-box:

Fig. 6

2. How many cubic inches are there in the volume of this brick?

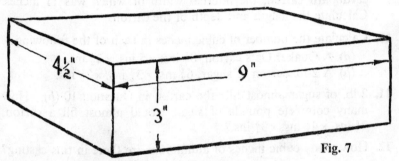

Fig. 7

3. Here is a dimensional sketch of an ordinary petrol tin (Fig. 8). Calculate the volume of the tin in cubic inches.

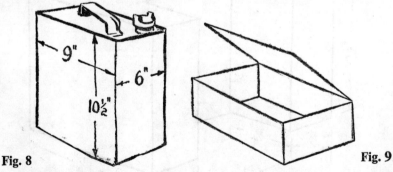

Fig. 8   Fig. 9

4. The internal dimensions of this cigar-box (Fig. 9) are: length, 9 ins.; breadth, $5\frac{1}{2}$ ins.; depth, $2\frac{3}{4}$ ins.
Calculate its volume in cubic inches.

5. How many match-boxes, like that shown in Fig. 6, could be packed lengthwise into the cigar-box in Fig. 9, no match-box to be packed on either its edge or its end?

6. How far from the top of the cigar-box would the top of the highest layer of match-boxes be?

7. A dozen boxes of matches, each 2 ins. $\times 1\frac{1}{2}$ ins. $\times \frac{1}{2}$ in. (see Fig. 6), are packed on edge in four layers, three boxes in each layer. Calculate the dimensions of the package.

8. A $\frac{1}{2}$-lb. slab of margarine measures $4\frac{1}{2}$ ins. $\times 2\frac{3}{4}$ ins. $\times 1\frac{1}{2}$ ins. Calculate the number of cubic inches in 1 lb. of margarine.

9. 48 $\frac{1}{2}$-lb. slabs of margarine were packed tightly in four layers in a cardboard carton, the internal width of which was 11 inches. Calculate the length and depth of the carton.

10. Calculate the number of cubic inches in each of the following:
   (a) A Quaker Oats carton, $8\frac{1}{2}$ ins. $\times 5$ ins. $\times 2\frac{1}{2}$ ins.
   (b) A 2-lb. carton of sugar, $6\frac{1}{2}$ ins. $\times 3\frac{3}{4}$ ins. $\times 2\frac{1}{2}$ ins.

11. 2 lb. of sugar almost fills the carton in Question 10 (b). How many complete pounds of sugar would almost fill a carton, $7\frac{1}{2}$ ins. $\times 4\frac{1}{2}$ ins. $\times 3\frac{3}{4}$ ins.?

12. How many cubic inches of aluminium are there in this casting?

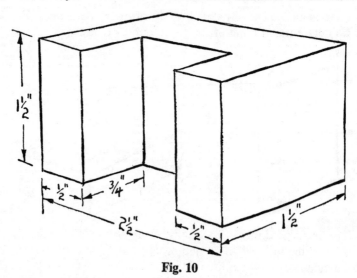

Fig. 10

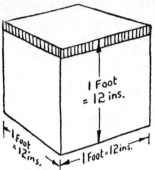

Fig. 11

Here is a sketch of a cube, the edges of which are 1 foot long. In other words, this is a sketch of a *cubic foot*. How many cubic inches could be cut from it?

First, we could cut from it, twelve slabs, each 1 inch thick, like the one shown shaded at the top of the sketch; and out of each slab we could cut 12×12 cubic inches; that is, 144 cu. ins. Therefore, altogether, we could cut 12×144 cu. ins. $= 1728$ cu. ins. You should commit this result to memory:

$$\text{`` 1 cubic foot} = 12 \times 12 \times 12 \text{ cubic inches}$$
$$= 1728 \text{ cubic inches.''}$$

What fraction of a cubic foot is the block of wood,

$$12 \text{ ins.} \times 4 \text{ ins.} \times 4 \text{ ins.,}$$

which is shown in the sketch on page 60.

Its volume, as we saw, is $12 \times 4 \times 4$ cubic inches.
One cubic foot contains $12 \times 12 \times 12$ cubic inches.

Therefore, the block $= \dfrac{12 \times 4 \times 4}{12 \times 12 \times 12}$ of a cubic foot.

Cancelling, we get $= \dfrac{1 \times 1 \times 1}{1 \times 3 \times 3} = \dfrac{1}{9}$ of a cubic foot.

We might have worked this entirely in fractions as follows:

Length $= 1$ ft.; breadth $= \dfrac{1}{3}$ of a ft.; thickness $= \dfrac{1}{3}$ of a ft.

Therefore, volume $= 1 \times \dfrac{1}{3} \times \dfrac{1}{3}$ of a cubic ft.

$= \dfrac{1}{9}$ of a cubic ft.

As another example of finding the volume in cubic feet of a rectangular object, by working entirely in fractions, let us find the volume of the brick shown in Fig 7.

First we express the length, breadth, and thickness, as fractions of a foot.

$$\text{Length} = 9 \text{ ins.}$$
$$= \frac{3}{4} \text{ of a ft.};$$
$$\text{Breadth} = 4\tfrac{1}{2} \text{ ins.}$$
$$= \frac{3}{8} \text{ of a ft.} \quad \text{(because } 4\tfrac{1}{2} \text{ ins.} = 3 \text{ times } 1\tfrac{1}{2} \text{ ins.,}$$
$$\text{and } 1\tfrac{1}{2} \text{ ins.} = \tfrac{1}{8} \text{ of a ft.)}$$
$$\text{Thickness} = 3 \text{ ins.}$$
$$= \frac{1}{4} \text{ of a ft.}$$

Therefore,
$$\text{Volume} = \frac{3}{4} \times \frac{3}{8} \times \frac{1}{4} \text{ of a cubic ft.}$$
$$= \frac{9}{128} \text{ of a cubic ft.}$$

This fraction of a cubic foot, $\frac{9}{128}$, seems a rather awkward fraction, but from it we can find the approximate number of bricks that make a cubic foot of brickwork. This is very useful for a bricklayer, or a man who repairs property, to know. This is how we find out the number:

$$1 \text{ brick} = \frac{9}{128} \text{ of a cubic ft;}$$

so, $128 \text{ bricks} = 128 \times \frac{9}{128}$ of a cubic ft. (Now cancel by 128)
$$= 1 \times \frac{9}{1} \text{ of a cubic ft.}$$
$$= 9 \text{ cubic ft.}$$

Now, if there are 128 bricks in 9 cubic feet, we must divide 128 by 9 in order to find the number of bricks in 1 cubic foot. That is, in 1 cubic foot there are $\frac{128}{9}$ bricks, that is, rather more than 14 bricks. A bricklayer, therefore, reckons about 14 bricks to a cubic foot.

EXERCISE XX

1. What fraction of a foot is 7 inches?

A plank of wood is 16 ft. long, 7 ins. wide, 3 ins. thick. Calculate its volume in cubic feet.

2. What would be the cost, at 12s. a cubic foot, of the following planks:

    1 plank 12 ft. long, 8 ins. wide, 3 ins. thick?
    2 planks 18 ft. long, 7 ins. wide, 4 ins. thick?
    2 planks 16 ft. long, 7 ins. wide, 2 ins. thick?

(*Note.* Timber merchants usually write the size of a plank like this: 12 ft. × 9 ins. × 3 ins.; instead of writing 12 ft. long, and so forth.)

3. What would be the cost, at 10s. 6d. a cubic foot, of the following planks:

    2 planks 14 ft. × 9 ins. × 3 ins.?
    3 planks 12 ft. × 7 ins. × 2½ ins.?
    2 planks 13 ft. × 11 ins. × 3 ins.?

4. What is the volume of brickwork in a garden wall 16 feet long, 3 feet high, 9 ins. thick?

How many bricks, approximately, would be needed to build it? (Reckon 14 bricks per cubic foot.)

5. Fig. 12 is a plan of a coal-bin built of brickwork, 4½ inches thick, and 3 feet high.

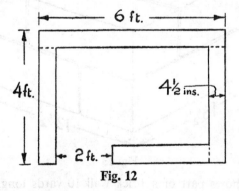

Fig. 12

Calculate the volume of brickwork in the walls in cubic feet, and the approximate number of bricks needed to build it.

6. You are to make a concrete path in part of the school garden. The length of the path is to be 20 feet; the width 1¼ yards; and the concrete is to be 4 inches thick. How many cubic feet of concrete would you need?

7. The coal-bin in Question 5 is built on a concrete platform 6 inches thick which extends 3 inches beyond the outside of the walls. Write down the length and width of this platform, and calculate the number of cubic feet of concrete needed to make it.

8. Calculate the number of cubic feet of timber in a gate-post 7 ft. 3 ins. × 8 ins. × 8 ins., and its cost at 9s. 6d. per cubic foot.

9. A portion of a school playground, 60 feet × 30 feet, is to be re-surfaced with tar macadam, 4 inches thick. How many cubic feet of tar macadam will be needed for it?

10 The tar macadam needed in Question 9 is to be carted from the gas-works in a truck, 8 feet long, 4 feet wide, 18 inches deep. How many loads of tar macadam will be needed?

11. Calculate the number of bricks needed for a pair of brick gate-posts, 5 feet 6 inches high, the bricks being laid in layers, or courses, like this:

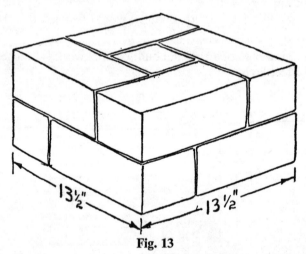

Fig. 13

12. Fig. 14 shows part of a brick wall 10 yards long, 6 feet high, 9 inches thick, standing on a concrete foundation 18 inches wide, 12 inches thick.

Fig. 14

Calculate the number of cubic feet of concrete needed for the foundation, and the number of cubic feet of brickwork in the wall.

Calculate, also, to the nearest half-thousand, the number of bricks in the wall.

Density

What do we mean by " The Density of a Substance "? The density of any material: wood, metal, brick, stone, etc., is the weight per unit volume. For instance,

> the weight per cubic inch,
> or, the weight per cubic foot,
> or, the weight per cubic yard, and so on.

This is how we find the density of a given material. First, we weigh a piece of the material; then we calculate its volume, either in cubic inches, or in cubic feet. From these two facts: the weight, and the volume, we find the weight per cubic inch or the weight per cubic foot.

F

Here is an example.

The block of wood, 12 ins. × 4 ins. × 4 ins., shown in Fig. 2, was a piece of beech. Let us find the density of beech, *in lb. per cubic foot*.

We weigh it, either by means of a spring balance, or on a household dial weighing machine.

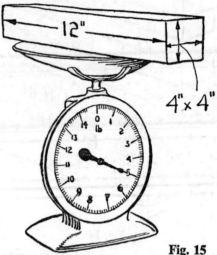

Fig. 15

We see from the sketch of the machine (Fig. 15) that the block of beech weighs 5 lb.

The volume of the block = 1 ft. × $\frac{1}{3}$ ft. × $\frac{1}{3}$ ft.

$$= \frac{1}{9} \text{ of a cubic foot.}$$

Thus, $\frac{1}{9}$ cu. ft. of beech weighs 5 lb.; therefore,

1 cu. ft. of beech weighs   5 lb. × 9
= 45 lb.

That is, the density of beech is 45 *lb. per cubic foot*.

Let us find the density of beech in *ounces per cubic inch*.

The weight of the block = 5 lb.
= 5 × 16 oz.

(*Note.* It is better not to multiply this out at this stage because we may find it convenient to cancel later.)

The volume of the block $= 12 \times 4 \times 4$ cu. ins.;

therefore, $12 \times 4 \times 4$ cu. ins. of beech weighs 5×16 oz.;

so,   1 cu. in. of beech weighs $\dfrac{5 \times 16}{12 \times 4 \times 4}$ oz.;

cancelling by 4×4, we get,

1 cu. in. of beech weighs $\dfrac{5 \times 1}{12 \times 1 \times 1}$ oz.

$$= \frac{5}{12} \text{ of an oz.}$$

Therefore, the density of beech is $\dfrac{5}{12}$ *of an ounce per cubic inch.*

In the table of densities on page 71 we read, the density of beech is

0·42 oz. per cubic inch.

Let us see how to turn the fraction, $\dfrac{5}{12}$, into a decimal, and so check the density given in the table of densities.

It is not always possible to express a vulgar fraction *exactly* as a decimal, but we can get an answer to any degree of accuracy we may wish; to the nearest tenth; to the nearest hundredth; to the nearest thousandth; and so forth.

First, let us find the value of $\dfrac{5}{12}$ of an oz. to the nearest tenth of an ounce.

To do this we change the 5 ounces into 50 tenths of an ounce, and divide by 12.

$$
\begin{array}{r}
\text{4 tenths of an oz.} \\
\hline
12 \,\big|\; \text{50 tenths of an oz.} \\
\text{2 tenths of an oz. remainder.}
\end{array}
$$

Thus, $\dfrac{5}{12}$ of an ounce lies between 4 tenths of an oz. and 5 tenths of an oz.; or, writing the tenths in the decimal notation,

$\dfrac{5}{12}$ of an ounce lies between ·4 of an oz.

and ·5 of an oz.

Since the remainder, when we divide by 12 is only 2 (which is less than half of 12), we say the answer is nearer to ·4 of an oz. than to ·5 of an oz.; so we say,

$\dfrac{5}{12}$ of an oz. $=$ ·4 of an oz. *to the nearest tenth.*

Next, let us find the value of $\frac{5}{12}$ of an ounce to the nearest hundredth of an ounce.

To do this, we change the 5 ounces into 500 hundredths of an ounce, and divide by 12.

$$
\begin{array}{r}
41 + \text{hundredths of an oz.} \\
\hline
12 \,\big|\, 500 \text{ hundredths of an oz.} \\
20 \\
8 \text{ hundredths of an oz. remainder.}
\end{array}
$$

Thus $\frac{5}{12}$ of an ounce lies between 41 hundredths of an oz., and 42 hundredths of an oz.; or, writing the hundredths in the decimal notation, we say,

$$\frac{5}{12} \text{ of an ounce lies between } \cdot41 \text{ of an oz.}$$
$$\text{and } \cdot42 \text{ of an oz.}$$

It is nearer to ·42 of an oz. because the remainder when we divide by 12 is 8 (which is greater than half of 12). Thus, we may write,

the density of beech is ·42 oz. per cu. in.

We could have calculated the density of beech, in ounces per cubic inches, directly from the density in pounds per cubic foot which we calculated on page 68, namely,

45 lb. per cubic foot.

To do it by this method, we change the 45 lb. into oz. by multiplication by 16, and then divide by 1728, since there are 1728 cubic inches in a cubic foot.

Here are the details of the calculation:

<table>
<tr><td></td><td>Working</td></tr>
<tr><td>45 lb. = 45 × 16 oz.</td><td>45 × 16</td></tr>
<tr><td>= 720 oz.</td><td>450</td></tr>
<tr><td></td><td>270</td></tr>
<tr><td></td><td>720</td></tr>
</table>

1728 cu. ins. of beech weighs   720 oz.

1 cu. in. of beech weighs $\frac{720}{1728}$ of an oz.

Since we want the density to the nearest hundredth of an ounce per

cubic inch, we change the 720 oz. into hundredths of an oz., and
divide by 1728.

$$720 \text{ oz.} = 72000 \text{ hundredths of an oz.}$$

$$\begin{array}{r} 41 + \text{ hundredths of an oz.} \\ 1728 \overline{\smash{\big)}\ 72000 \text{ hundredths of an oz.}} \\ 6912 \\ \hline 2880 \\ 1728 \\ \hline 1152 \text{ hundredths of an oz. remainder.} \end{array}$$

The result lies between 41 hundredths of an oz. and 42 hundredths
of an oz., but it is nearer to 42 hundredths, since the remainder is
1152 hundredths, and this is greater than one-half of the divisor,
1728, so we write,

the density of beech is ·42 oz. per cu. in.;

the result which we got before, and the same as that given in the
table below.

Use this table of densities when necessary in the questions in
Exercise XXI.

Materials	Densities in lb. per cu. ft.	Densities in oz. per cu. in.
Yellow Pine	28 lb. per cu. ft.	
Red Pine	35 lb. per cu. ft.	
Pitch Pine	41 lb. per cu. ft.	
Beech	45 lb. per cu. ft.	0·42 oz. per cu. in.
Oak	50 lb. per cu. ft.	
Limestone	145 lb. per cu. ft.	
Brickwork (in mortar)	112 lb. per cu. ft.	
Concrete	126 lb. per cu. ft.	
Aluminium	168 lb. per cu. ft.	
Cast Iron	448 lb. per cu. ft.	
Copper	·548 lb. per cu. ft.	

EXERCISE XXI

1. Calculate, to the nearest hundredth of an ounce, the density in ounces per cubic inch of each of the following:

oak, yellow pine, pitch pine, red pine, aluminium, cast iron, copper.

2. Calculate the weight in pounds of a plank, 12 ft. × 7 ins. × 3 ins., of each of the following timbers:

yellow pine, pitch pine, oak, beech.

3. How much would a block of concrete measuring

2 ft. 6 ins. × 6 ins. × 6 ins. weigh?

4. What would be the weight of a slab of limestone,

2 ft. 6 ins. × 1 ft. 6 ins. × 9 ins.?

5. Calculate the total weight of the following:

5 planks of red pine,   16 ft. × 11 ins. × 3 ins.,
8 planks of pitch pine,   15 ft. × 9 ins. × 3 ins.,
12 planks of yellow pine, 14 ft. × 7 ins. × 3 ins.

6. A lorry was loaded with the following lengths of 6 ins. × 1 in. red pine flooring boards:

30 @ 16 ft.; 36 @ 14 ft.; 28 @ 13 ft.; 50 @ 12 ft.

Calculate the number of cubic feet of timber in the load, and its total weight.

7. The framework of an oak garden gate consisted of the following:

2 stiles (uprights), 4 ft. × 5 ins. × 2 ins.
1 top rail,   3 ft. 9 ins. × 5 ins. × 2 ins.
1 middle rail,   3 ft. 9 ins. × 6 ins. × 2 ins.
1 bottom rail,   3 ft. 9 ins. × 7 ins. × 2 ins.

Calculate the number of cubic feet of oak in the gate, and the approximate weight when made, neglecting the waste in making the joints.

8. Calculate the approximate weight of a pitch pine garden gate-post 7 ft. long; cross-section, 8 ins. × 8 ins.

9. Calculate the weight per foot of length of a copper bar

3 ins. × $\frac{1}{2}$ in. cross-section.

10. A pattern-maker made a wooden pattern from which to cast a number of blocks of the sizes and shape shown in this sketch:

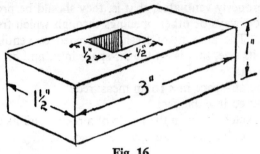

Fig. 16

Calculate, (*a*) the volume of the casting in cubic inches;
(*b*) the weight of 12 cast-iron castings made from that pattern.

11. Calculate the volume, and the weight of each of the aluminium castings shown in the dimensioned sketches below.

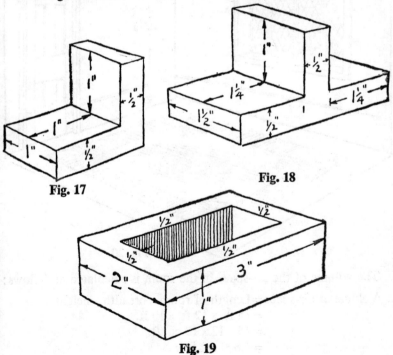

Fig. 17

Fig. 18

Fig. 19

Air-space and ventilation

All rooms in which people live, work, or take their recreation should be properly ventilated, that is, they should be provided with windows, doorways or other openings through which fresh air may enter them. The amount of fresh air needed to ventilate a room depends on its size, that is on the air-space in it, and on the number of its occupants.

How is the air-space in a room measured?

It is measured in cubic feet.

Here is a sketch showing the inside of a room, and its dimensions. How many cubic feet of air-space are there in it?

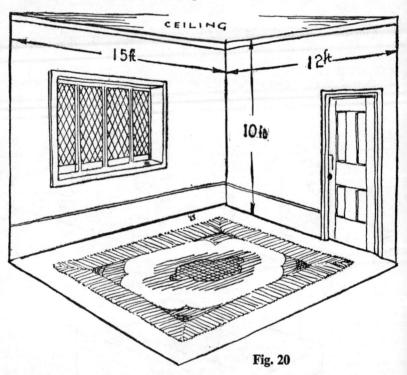

Fig. 20

The volume of the air-space in the room is calculated as follows:

Volume of air-space = Length of room × breadth × height
= 15 ft. × 12 ft. × 10 ft.
= 15 × 12 × 10 cu. ft.
= 1,800 cu. ft.

Another example:

A classroom for 30 pupils is 24 ft. × 22 ft. 6 ins.; the height of the ceiling is 10 ft.

Calculate the total air-space in the room, and the air-space per pupil.

The total air-space $= 24$ ft. $\times 22\frac{1}{2}$ ft. $\times 10$ ft.

$$= 24 \times 22\frac{1}{2} \times 10 \text{ cu. ft.}$$

$$= 5,400 \text{ cu. ft.}$$

Air-space per pupil $= 5,400 \div 30$ cu. ft.

$$= 180 \text{ cu. ft.}$$

Now, an adult needs, at least, 1,000 cubic feet of fresh air every hour. It is a regulation in most towns that the ventilation of buildings used by the public—cinemas, theatres, public halls, and so forth —must be based upon the supply of at least that amount of fresh air per hour.

On this basis, how long would the air in the classroom last without change?

1,000 cubic feet of air would last 1 hour;

180 cubic feet would last $\dfrac{180}{1000}$ of an hour

$$= \frac{180 \times 60}{1000} \text{ minutes}$$

$$= \frac{10800}{1000} \text{ minutes}$$

$$= 10 \cdot 8 \text{ minutes.}$$

Therefore the air should be completely changed at least six times every hour.

The fresh air needed to ventilate a room should not cause draughts. For this reason, the grids that admit it are usually placed round a room, a little above floor level, and the outlet grids are placed near the ceiling.

A bedroom fitted with sash windows is most satisfactorily ventilated by raising the lower sash a little to admit fresh air, and lowering the upper sash to act as an outlet.

EXERCISE XXII

In the following questions, when necessary, assume that every person needs 1,000 cubic feet of fresh air per hour.

1. Calculate the total air-space in a bedroom 12 ft. × 12 ft.; ceiling-height, 9 ft.

2. Calculate the air-space in a classroom 24 ft. × 30 ft., height, 10 ft. 6 ins.

3. Calculate the air-space in each of the following rooms in a cottage:

   Living-room,   14 ft. × 12 ft. × 9 ft.;
   Kitchen,   12 ft. × 10 ft. × 9 ft.;
   Bedroom,   13 ft. × 11 ft. × 9 ft.;
   Bedroom,   13 ft. × 10 ft. × 9 ft.;
   Bedroom,   11 ft. × 10 ft. × 9 ft.

4. Calculate the air-space in each of the following rooms:

   Ground floor: Dining-room,   14 ft. × 13 ft. × 10 ft.;
                  Lounge,   17 ft. × 14 ft. × 10 ft.;
                  Kitchen,   12 ft. × 12 ft. × 10 ft.;
                  Scullery,   12 ft. × 9 ft. × 10 ft.
   First floor: Bedroom,   17 ft. × 14 ft. × 9 ft.;
                  Bedroom,   14 ft. × 13 ft. × 9 ft.;
                  Bedroom,   12 ft. × 10 ft. × 9 ft.;
                  Bathroom,   12 ft. × 9 ft. × 9 ft.

5. A classroom for 30 pupils was 24 ft. × 22 ft. 6 ins. Calculate the floor-space per pupil.

6. In a restaurant the seating accommodation allowed for an average of 8 square feet per customer. The ceiling was 10 feet high.

   Calculate (a) the air-space per customer;
                (b) the number of times per hour that the air in the restaurant should be changed.

7. Allowing an average of 8 square feet per person in a church, the height of which was 50 feet, calculate the number of times per hour that the air should be changed.

8. Two brothers sleep in a bedroom 14 ft. × 12 ft. × 9 ft. How many times an hour should the air in the room be changed if the boys are to remain healthy?

9. A railway compartment, with seating accommodation for 10 passengers, is 9 feet long, 7 feet wide. The average height is 7 feet 6 inches.

   Calculate (a) the total air-space in the compartment;
   (b) the average air-space per passenger;
   (c) the number of times the air should be changed in a journey lasting half an hour.

10. The height of the ceiling of the classroom in Question 5 was 12 feet. Calculate the total air-space in the room, and the number of times the air should be changedper hour.

11. A school dining-room is 60 feet by 22 feet 6 inches. The height of the ceiling is 15 feet. The seating accommodation is sufficient for 180 pupils.

   Calculate the average air-space per pupil, and the number of times per hour that the air should be changed.

12. The cubical capacity—that is, the total air-space—in a certain public hall is 420,000 cubic feet. The seating accommodation is sufficient for 1,850 persons.

   Calculate (a) the air-space per person;
   (b) the number of times per hour that the air in it should be changed.

13. Here are some particulars relating to a cinema:

   Floor-space, 80 ft. × 60 ft.
   Average height, 27 ft.
   Seating accommodation, 750.

   Calculate (a) the number of cubic feet of air-space per person when the cinema is full;
   (b) the number of times an hour that the air should be changed.

14. The new House of Commons has seating accommodation for 637 members. Its cubical capacity is 174,000 cubic feet.

   Calculate (a) the cubical capacity per member;
   (b) the number of times an hour that the air should be changed.

A gas meter

A gas meter is a contrivance for measuring, in cubic feet, the gas which is consumed in a household or on other premises. This is a drawing of the dial which the gas-man reads when he comes to the house, about once a quarter.

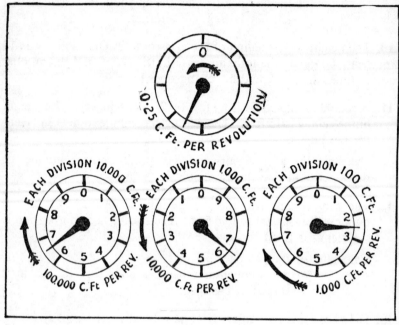

Fig. 21

At the top, there is a circle divided into 8 parts, and near it, it says " 0·25 cu. ft. per revolution " [that is, $\frac{1}{4}$ cu. ft. per revolution]. This is chiefly used by gas engineers when making tests.

In a row at the bottom of the panel, there are three—sometimes four—circles, each divided into 10 parts.

Starting from the right, the indicator turns round in clockwise direction, every division turned through representing a consumption of 100 cubic feet of gas; that is, 1,000 cu. ft. per revolution.

The hand or indicator on the next circle, turns in the opposite direction, that is counter-clockwise, and each division through which it turns indicates a consumption of 1,000 cu. ft. of gas. The hand on the next, that is the third, circle rotates as the first did, that is, in a clockwise direction, and each division through which it turns represents a consumption of 10,000 cu. ft. of gas.

At the end of March the gas-man *read* the dials and entered the reading in his book as 54,700 cubic feet.

At the end of June, he found the dials as shown in Fig. 21. What should he now enter in his book? How much gas had been consumed between the dates of the two readings of the meter?

Here is a copy of the readings of a domestic gas-meter taken at the ends of thirteen successive quarters:

	31st December	311,900
First Year	31st March	318,500
	30th June	325,400
	30th September	329,500
	31st December	334,500
Second Year	31st March	340,700
	30th June	343,000
	30th September	346,700
	31st December	350,200
Third Year	31st March	354,500
	30th June	357,700
	30th September	360,500
	31st December	364,500

From these readings it is interesting to make comparisons of the amount of gas consumed during corresponding periods in consecutive years.

For example: Compare the amount of gas consumed during the Second Year with that consumed during the First Year.

Reading on Dec. 31st of the First Year was   334,500 cu. ft.
Reading on Dec. 31st of the preceding Year was 311,900 cu. ft.
    Consumption during First Year was   22,600 cu. ft.

Reading on Dec. 31st of the Second Year was   350,200 cu. ft.
Reading on Dec. 31st of the First Year was   334,500 cu. ft.
    Consumption during the Second Year was   15,700 cu. ft.

More calculations based upon this record of the gas-meter readings will be found in the following exercise.

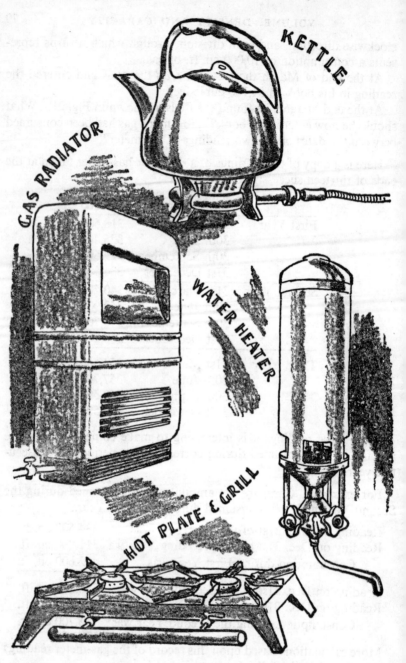

KETTLE

GAS RADIATOR

WATER HEATER

HOT PLATE & GRILL

EXERCISE XXIII

1. It took 8 minutes to boil a 4-pint kettleful of water on a gas-ring. During that time the indicator in the top circle of the dial made two complete revolutions. Calculate:

    (*a*) the total amount of gas consumed in boiling 4 pints of water;

    (*b*) the consumption of gas by the gas-ring, in cubic feet per minute.

2. A gas-radiator consumes 0·25 cubic feet of gas in 2 minutes. What is the hourly consumption in cubic feet?

3. How many minutes would it take to consume 1 cubic foot of gas

    (*a*) on the gas-ring in Question 1?

    (*b*) in the gas-radiator in Question 2?

4. The gas-radiator in Question 2 was used, on an average, for 4 hours a day during the month of November. What is the cost of the gas consumed at 4s. 9d. per 1,000 cubic feet?

5. A sink water-heater consumes 60 cubic feet of gas per hour. On an average it is used for 5 minutes, 6 times a day. What will be the approximate cost per week when gas is 5s. per thousand cubic feet?

6. The consumption of a hot-plate and grill is 35 cubic feet per hour. It took 2 hours to cook a meal on it. What would this cost when the price of gas is 4s. 9d. per thousand cubic feet?

7. Here is an extract from a gas bill.

    To Gas Supplied

Present Meter Reading	298,300 cu. ft.
Previous Meter Reading	289,900 cu. ft.
Gas Consumed	8,400 cu. ft. at 5s. per 1,000 cu. ft.

    Calculate the amount of the gas bill for that quarter.

    In Questions 8 to 12 use the record of gas-meter readings on page 79.

8. Calculate the amount of gas consumed during each of the quarters December to March, March to June, June to September, and September to December in the First Year.

9. Calculate the average consumption of gas per day during the December to March quarter of the First Year, that is from January 1st to March 31st inclusive, reckoning 28 days in February.

10. Calculate the amount of gas consumed during each of the quarters in the Second Year, and compare these with the consumption in the corresponding quarters in the First Year. (See Question 8.)

(You will see that the consumption during the first quarters in the two years was almost unchanged, but in the other quarters of the Second Year it was much less than during the corresponding quarters in the First Year. The reason for this is a change in the method of cooking. A new cooker, which uses coke, installed in March of the Second Year, was used for most of the cooking.)

11. Calculate the amount of gas consumed during each of the quarters December to March, March to June, June to September, and September to December in the Third Year.

12. Using the results that you got in answers to Questions 8 and 10, calculate the cost of gas consumed during the three quarters from March to December in each of the two years, at the rate of 5s. per 1,000 cubic feet.

13. Calculate, at the rate of 5s. per 1,000 cubic feet, the cost of the gas consumed during each of the three years shown in the meter-readings.

14. During the three quarters from March to December in the Second Year, three-quarters of a ton of coke were needed for the cooker. The coke cost 4s. 6d. per hundredweight. Which was the greater, the cost of gas for the three quarters of the First Year, or the combined cost of gas and coke for the corresponding quarters of the Second Year?

Finding the volume of an irregularly shaped thing

How shall we find the volume of an irregularly shaped body such as a lump of coal?

Have you ever heard the story which tells how Archimedes, a learned Greek who lived in the island of Sicily nearly 300 years before the birth of Christ, found out that a crown that had been made for a king was not pure gold, as it should have been?

Well, it is something like this. Archimedes weighed the crown, and then, for a long time he was puzzled. He said, " If only I could find the volume of the crown I could reckon how much it *should* weigh if it were pure gold." One day when he was in his bath, so we are told, an idea struck him. He saw the water rise up the sides of the bath when he got into it, so he thought " surely, by measuring the height that the water has risen, I can find the volume of my body ". He jumped out of the bath, so the story goes, and ran outside calling out, in his language, " I've found it; I've found it", meaning, of course, he had discovered the way to find the volume of the crown. He then immersed the crown in a vessel containing water; found its volume; and calculated what it should weigh if it were pure gold. He found it was not the right weight, so he was able to tell the king that the crown was not pure gold.

Thus we now see one method of finding the volume of an irregularly shaped body such as a lump of coal: the immersion method.

Take a tank, like an aquarium tank, containing water. Fix a piece of gummed paper at the level of the water as shown in (Fig. 22).

Now lower the lump of coal, or other irregularly shaped body into the water by means of a piece of string. The level of the water will rise; the larger the lump, the higher it will rise.

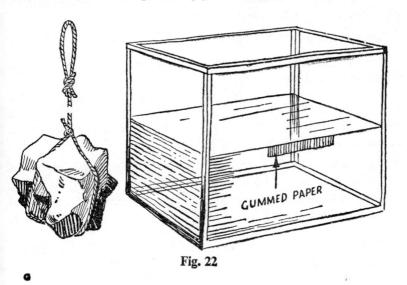

GUMMED PAPER

Fig. 22

G

What measurements shall we need in order to calculate the volume of the lump of coal?

We shall need:

(*a*) the area of the surface of the water in the tank;
(*b*) the height that the surface rises above the gummed paper.

The volume will then be the product of the area of the surface, and the rise in level during the experiment.

For example, if the internal measurements of the tank at the surface of the water were 9 inches by 8 inches; and the surface rose 2 inches, we should have:

(*a*) the area of the surface of the water $= 9$ ins. $\times 8$ ins.
$= 72$ sq. ins.
(*b*) the rise of the surface $= 2$ ins.
The volume of the body $= 72 \times 2$ cu. ins.
$= 144$ cu. ins.

We can use another method of finding the volume of an irregularly snaped body when we know the density of the material of which it is comprised: the density method.

We weigh the body, say, a piece of aluminium, either by means of a spring balance, or by some scales. Let its weight be 7·32 oz.

From the table of densities on page 71 we find the density of aluminium to be 1·5 oz. per cubic inch.

The volume $= \dfrac{7 \cdot 32}{1 \cdot 5}$ cubic inches.

Here a little difficulty may arise because the divisor is not a whole number; it contains a decimal.

There are many ways of dividing by a decimal. Most of the ways are very confusing. By far the best way for many people is to find first the approximate answer by the use of a little common sense, something like this:

the volume must be greater than 4 cu. ins. because 4 cu. ins. of aluminium weigh 1·5 oz. $\times 4 = 6 \cdot 0$ oz.;

the volume must be less than 5 cu. ins. because 5 cu. ins. of aluminium weigh 1·5 oz. $\times 5 = 7 \cdot 5$ oz.

Therefore, the answer to the division $\dfrac{7 \cdot 32}{1 \cdot 5}$ cu. ins. lies between 4 cu. ins. and 5 cu. ins.

Since we have to express the answer to the nearest hundredth of a cu. in. we shall need three digits in it; the whole number, which we have already found, namely, 4; and two places of decimal.

At this stage we ignore entirely the decimal points in both the numerator and the denominator, so as to avoid confusion, and divide by ordinary long division until we have three digits in the answer. Then we insert the decimal point in its right place.

Here is the completion of the working:

$$
\begin{array}{r}
488 \\
15\overline{\smash{\big)}732} \\
60 \\
\hline
132 \\
120 \\
\hline
120 \\
120 \\
\hline
\cdots
\end{array}
$$

Therefore, the volume = 4·88 cu. ins.

Here is another example which we shall work, without the explanation, in order to show that the process of dividing by a decimal is really very simple.

A piece of beech (density ·42 oz. per cu. in.), weighs 2·75 oz. What is its volume to the nearest hundredth of a cubic inch?

$$\text{Volume} = \frac{2\cdot75}{\cdot42} \text{ cu. ins.}$$

The volume lies between 6 cu. ins. and 7 cu. ins., because

$$\cdot42 \text{ oz.} \times 6 = 2\cdot52 \text{ oz.}$$
$$\text{and} \quad \cdot42 \text{ oz.} \times 7 = 2\cdot94 \text{ oz.}$$

$$
\begin{array}{r}
654+ \\
42\overline{\smash{\big)}275} \\
252 \\
\hline
230 \\
210 \\
\hline
200 \\
168 \\
\hline
32 \text{ (more than half the divisor).}
\end{array}
$$

Therefore, the volume = 6·55 cu. ins. to the nearest hundredth.

EXERCISE XXIV

1. A lump of sandstone was completely immersed in a rectangular tank containing water. The surface of the water in the tank which was 8 inches long, and 6 inches wide, rose 2·7 inches. Calculate the volume of the stone in cubic inches.

2. The stone in Question 1 weighed 9·6 lb. Calculate the density of the stone in ounces per cubic inch.

3. This hook was completely immersed in the same tank as was used in Question 1. The surface of the water rose 0·65 of an inch. Calculate the volume of the hook in cubic inches.

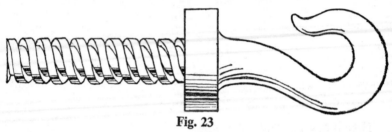

Fig. 23

4. The hook in Question 3 weighed 7·8 lb. Calculate the density of the material of which the hook was made, in ounces per cubic inch.

5. A piece of copper weighed 11·8 ounces. The density of copper is 5·07 oz. per cubic inch. Calculate the volume of the copper in cubic inches to the nearest hundredth of a cubic inch.

6. An aluminium casting weighed 370·6 lb. The density of aluminium is 168·2 lb. per cu. ft. Calculate the volume of the casting to the nearest hundredth of a cubic foot.

7. A metal casting was completely immersed in water in a 3-lb. jam jar, the cross-sectional area of which was 12·5 square inches. The surface of the water rose 1·4 ins. Calculate the volume of the casting in cubic inches.

8. A copper casting weighed 33·5 ounces. Calculate its volume. (The density of copper is 5·07 oz. per cu. in.)

9. A casting was immersed in a jam jar containing water. The level of the water rose one-third of an inch. The internal cross-sectional area of the jam jar was 12 square inches. Calculate the volume of the casting.

10. Eighty steel ball bearings such as are used in the hubs of a bicycle weigh $1\frac{1}{2}$ ounces.

They were dropped into a small medicine bottle containing water. The surface of the water rose $\frac{1}{4}$ of an inch (Fig. 24). The internal cross-section of the medicine bottle was $1\frac{1}{2}$ inches $\times \frac{2}{3}$ of an inch.

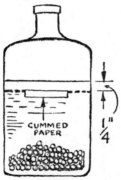

Fig. 24

Calculate (*a*) The area of the cross-section of the bottle;

            (*b*) The volume of the eighty steel balls;

            (*c*) the number of steel balls per cubic inch;

            (*d*) The density of steel in ounces per cubic inch.

11. From the result of Question 10 calculate the density of steel in pounds per cubic foot.

12. A block of oak, 2 ft. $\times$ 9 ins. $\times$ 6 ins., was put into a tank 3 feet long, 2 feet wide, containing some water. It floated with one-fifth of its volume above the surface of the water. The depth of of water in the tank before the oak was floated in it was 18 inches. Calculate the depth when the oak floated.

Capacity

The capacity of a vessel—a tank, a pail or bucket, a kettle, a jug, and so forth—is the measure of what it will hold.

We say, a tank will hold such-and-such a number of gallons; we speak of a three-gallon pail; of a 4-pint kettle; of a pint jug, and so on. These are all measures of capacity.

From the dimensions of a tank we can calculate the number of cubic feet of anything that it will hold. We are now to try to find the relation between gallons—or pints—and cubic feet.

A simple and fairly accurate method of doing so is this:

Fill a pint milk bottle, exactly to the ledge round the rim on which the cardboard cap rests, with fine dry sand. By patting the bottle a little, the sand will settle down, quite compact, in the bottle.

Now take an empty 1-lb. sugar carton, and take its internal dimensions, each to the nearest tenth of an inch. These dimensions are shown in (Fig. 25).

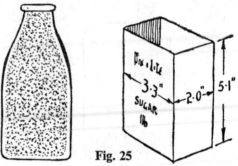

Fig. 25

Pour the sand from the milk bottle into the sugar carton, and pat the sides of the carton so that the sand settles down tightly in it. You may find about a spoonful of sand left over after the carton is full. This we shall neglect in the following calculation, as we are trying to find the approximate number of cubic inches in a pint.

The volume of sand in the carton = 5·1 × 3·3 × 2·0 cu. ins.

$$\begin{array}{r} 5\cdot1 \times 3\cdot3 \\ \hline 15\cdot3 \\ 1\cdot53 \\ \hline 16\cdot83 \times 2\cdot0 \\ \hline 33\cdot66 \text{ cu. ins.} \end{array}$$

Thus, the volume of the sand in the carton = 34 cu. ins. approx.
Therefore, 1 pint = 34 cubic inches, approximately.
This result will help us to find the number of pints in a cubic foot. In a cubic foot there are 1,728 cubic inches.
The number of times that 34 cubic inches is contained in 1,728 cubic inches is the number of pints in a cubic foot.

$$\begin{array}{r} 50 \\ 34\overline{)1728} \\ 170 \\ \hline 28 \end{array}$$

Thus, we see that there are approximately 50 pints in a cubic foot.

Here is another method of finding the number of pints in a cubic foot. It may be rather difficult to get the apparatus needed but if it can be got, you will find the experiment very interesting.

You need a tank, preferably a glass aquarium tank, about 12 ins. × 8 ins., 12 ins. deep (Fig. 26). (This will not hold a complete cubic foot of water, but half a cubic foot of water will stand 9 inches deep in it.)

You need also a weighing machine (one used for weighing school children will do very well) and a 1-pint milk bottle.

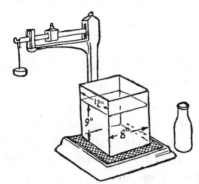

Fig. 26

Weigh the tank empty, and again when it holds half a cubic foot of water.

From these two weighings, by subtraction, you can find the weight of half-a-cubic-foot of water.

Now weigh an empty 1-pint milk bottle on a dial weighing machine like that shown on page 68. Fill the bottle with water, and weigh it again, and by subtraction, find the weight of 1 pint of water.

Here are the results of an experiment:

Weight of empty tank   = 16·25 lb.
Weight of tank and half a cubic foot of water = 47·5 lb.
Therefore, weight of water   = 31·25 lb. = 31¼ lb.
Weight of empty bottle   = 1 lb. 3 oz.
Weight of bottle and water   = 2 lb. 7 oz.
Therefore, weight of water   = 1 lb. 4 oz. = 1¼ lb.

Therefore the weight of half-a-cubic-foot of water is 31¼ lb., so

1 cubic foot of water weighs 62½ lb.

This result is very important: it should be committed to memory.

" A pint of water weighs a pound and a quarter," is worth remembering, too.

The number of pints in 1 cubic foot is found from these results by dividing the weight of a cubic foot of water by the weight of a pint of water.

Number of pints in 1 cubic foot $= \dfrac{62\frac{1}{2} \text{ lb.}}{1\frac{1}{4} \text{ lb.}}$

Express both numerator and the denominator in $\frac{1}{4}$-lb., and we get

The number of pints in 1 cubic foot $= \dfrac{250}{5}$ pints

$= 50$ pints.

This result is the one we shall use.

That is,

"There are 50 pints in a cubic foot."

Since there are 8 pints in a gallon,

1 gallon of water weighs $1\frac{1}{4} \times 8$ lb. $= 10$ lb.

Since, also, 1 cubic foot of water weighs $62\frac{1}{2}$ lb., and 1 gallon of water weighs 10 lb., there are $6\frac{1}{4}$ gallons in 1 cubic foot.

We now gather together these results for reference:

1. One pint of water weighs one pound and a quarter.
2. One gallon of water weighs 10 lb.
3. One cubic foot of water weighs $62\frac{1}{2}$ lb.
4. There are $6\frac{1}{4}$ gallons in one cubic foot.

Bulk-for-bulk, some liquids are lighter, some heavier, than water. For instance, a gallon of petrol weighs only 0·88 of the weight of a gallon of water; a pint of milk weighs 1·03 times as much as a pint of water. It is customary to express these facts in this way: The specific gravity of petrol is 0·88; the specific gravity of milk is 1·03.

Here is a table of specific gravities for use in connection with Questions 13 to 18 in Exercise XXV.

Liquid	Specific Gravity
Water	1·00
Petrol	0·88
Milk	1·03
Liquid in a fully charged car battery	1·28
Honey	1·45

During use, the specific gravity of the liquid in an accumulator falls. Garage-men test the specific gravity of car batteries—or accumulators—by means of an instrument called a *hydrometer*. Fig. 27 is an illustration of a garage hydrometer.

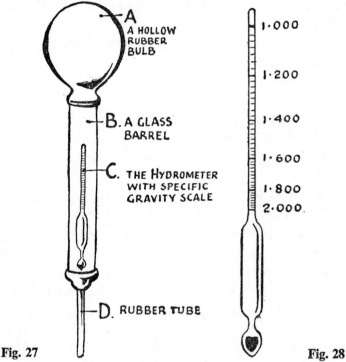

A
A HOLLOW
RUBBER
BULB

B. A GLASS
BARREL

C. THE HYDROMETER
WITH SPECIFIC
GRAVITY SCALE

D. RUBBER TUBE

1·000

1·200

1·400

1·600

1·800

2·000.

Fig. 27   Fig. 28

How to use a garage hydrometer.

Squeeze the rubber bulb and insert the end of the rubber tube into the battery liquid. Slowly release the pressure on the bulb until the specific gravity scale (Fig. 28) floats in the liquid that is drawn up from the battery cell. The specific gravity of the liquid in the cell of the battery is the reading on the scale at the surface of the liquid in the glass barrel. The numbers on the scale are lowest at the top, and highest at the bottom. (Can you explain why this is so?)

Government inspectors periodically visit farms and dairies to test the purity of the milk. They use hydrometers like the one shown, enlarged, in the illustration above. They float the hydrometer in a sample of milk, and read, on the scale, the specific gravity of the sample.

EXERCISE XXV

1. A 3-pint electric kettle, when empty, weighs $3\frac{1}{2}$ lb. What is its weight when full of water?

2. A 2-pint jug, when empty, weighs 1 lb. 6 oz. Calculate its weight when full of water.

3. A $1\frac{1}{2}$-gallon watering can weighs $1\frac{3}{4}$ lb. when empty. What is its weight when full of water?

4. A 2-gallon pail weighs 5 lb. when empty. Calculate its weight when full of water.

5. Using the table of specific gravities on page 90 calculate the weight of 1 gallon of petrol.

6. An empty 2-gallon petrol tin weighs $1\frac{1}{2}$ lb. Calculate its weight when full.

7. The specific gravity of milk is 1·03. Calculate the weight of 1 gallon of milk.

8. A 2-gallon milk can weighs $4\frac{1}{2}$ lb. when empty. What will be its weight when full?

9. An aluminium preserving pan weighs $2\frac{3}{4}$ lb. when empty. What will be its weight when it contains a gallon and a half of water?

10. In the bathroom of a house there is a cistern 2 feet long, 2 feet wide, and 1 foot 9 inches deep. How many gallons of water does it hold when the water surface is 3 inches from the top?

11. Calculate the weight of water in the cistern in Question 10.

12. How many thousands of gallons of water does it take to fill a swimming bath, 25 yards long, 10 yards wide to an average depth of 4 feet 6 inches?

13. Assuming that there are four cupfuls in a pint, calculate the weight of a cupful of milk.

14. What is the weight of a cupful of honey?

15. 2 lb. of common salt is dissolved in one gallon of water, forming one gallon of brine.

    Calculate (a) the combined weight of the salt and water;
    (b) the specific gravity of the brine.

16. A radio accumulator, when full, holds 1 pint of liquid. When fully charged, the specific gravity of the liquid should be 1·28. Calculate the weight of the liquid in a fully charged accumulator.

17. A garage man found that the specific gravity of the liquid in the cells of a car battery was 1·20, and that the cells needed " topping " with distilled water (specific gravity 1). Would the addition of the distilled water increase or decrease the specific gravity of the cell liquid?

18. The cells of a car battery were only three-quarters-full of liquid, at specific gravity 1·20. What would be the specific gravity after they were filled with distilled water.

19. Half a pint of milk and half a pint of water were mixed together. Calculate (*a*) the weight of the pint of milk and water, (*b*) the specific gravity of the mixture.

20. 5 ounces of sugar was dissolved in 1 pint of water. The volume of liquid was not appreciably changed. Calculate (*a*) the combined weight of the sugar and water, (*b*) the specific gravity of the sugar solution.

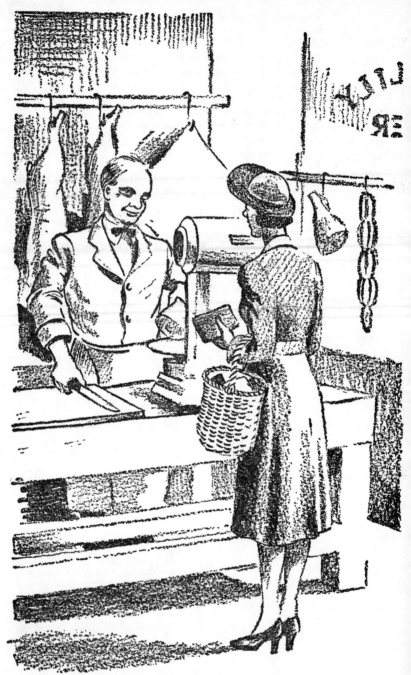

V

WEIGHING

At the butcher's shop

You have, no doubt, often been to the butcher's shop to buy meat.
If so, you will have noticed that the butcher uses scales for weighing
meat something like the one shown in the picture. On the customer's
side of the counter, there is a glass panel behind which, in the middle,
is visible a part of a rotating drum or cylinder on which lb. and oz.
are marked. The panel looks like this:

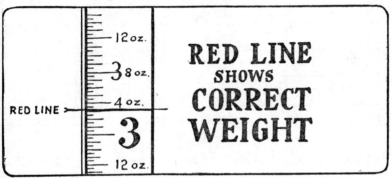

Fig. 1

while the customer is wondering how much a lb. it costs!

This seems a hard problem as it stands, but if we turn the 3 lb. 3 oz.
into oz., that is 51 oz., and the 4s. 3d. into pence, that is 51 pence, we
see that the cost is 1d. an oz., which is 1s. 4d. a lb.

If the cost per lb. were, say, 1s. 10d., the problem of reckoning the
cost of, say, 3 lb. 3oz. of meat would not be quite so easy, because the
cost per oz. would be one-sixteenth of 1s. 10d.; this would be $1\frac{6}{16}$d.
($1\frac{3}{8}$d.) exactly, or $1\frac{1}{2}$d. approximately for extra ounces.

Now, when the butcher has weighed the meat in lb. and oz. he
tells the customer how much he has to pay for it. He usually calls out
very quickly, as though he were a " lightning calculator ", something
like this:

3 lb. 3 oz. 4s. 3d.,

This would be the complete calculation, which would, of course, be done mentally,

$$3 \text{ lb. @ 1s. 10d.} = 5s. \ 6d.$$
$$3 \text{ oz. @ } 1\tfrac{1}{2}d. = 4\tfrac{1}{2}d.$$
$$\text{Total} = 5s. \ 10\tfrac{1}{2}d.$$

But the butcher, after putting the meat on the scales, would call out at once,

" 3 lb. 3 oz. . . . . . . 5s. 10d."

without any calculation at all.　How does he do it?　The secret lies in what he sees through the glass panel on *his* side of the scales.　This is what he sees:

THE BUTCHER'S VIEW OF THE WEIGHT AND COST CHART

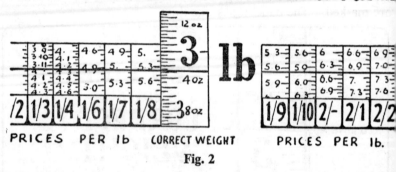

Fig. 2

A red line and prices per lb.—from 1s. per lb. to 2s. 3d. per lb.— are fixed on a glass panel.　Behind it there is a convenient form of ready-reckoner, showing the correct weight and the value or cost, printed on a drum which rotates when a weight is placed on the scales.

The red line points to the weight; in this case, 3 lb. 3 oz.; and it crosses the column above the price of 1s. 10d. per lb. at the place marked 5s. 10d.　Thus the cost of 3 lb. 3 oz. at 1s. 10d. per lb. is 5s. 10d.

Scales like this, which not only register automatically the weight placed on them but also shows in the form of an automatic ready reckoner the cost at a given price per lb. is a very clever invention, and a great time-saver to a shopkeeper.

The costs indicated on the scales are quite correct but sometimes mistakes occur in making up bills, so there is a need to be able to check them by calculation.

EXERCISE XXVI, Part One

1. Calculate, to the nearest half-penny, the cost per ounce at the following rates per pound:

1s. 2d.; 1s. 4d; 1s. 6d; 1s. 8d.; 1s. 10d.

2. What is the cost of 7 ounces of cheese at 1s. 5d. a pound? (It will be best to deduct the cost of 1 ounce from the cost of half-a-pound.)

3. Calculate the charges that should appear on the butcher's ready-reckoner panel for 2 lb. 7 oz. for prices per pound ranging from 1s. 4d. to 2s. 2d.

4. Is the following bill correct to the nearest half-penny?

Leg of mutton, 4 lb. 7 oz. @ 1s. 6d. per lb.; 6s. 8d.

5. What should be the charges for the following items in a boarding-house keeper's butcher's bill?

June 6th. Steak,   2 lb. 13 oz. @ 1s. 10d. per lb. . . . . . .
June 7th. Pork,   4 lb. 9 oz. @ 1s. 2d. per lb. . . . . . .
June 8th. Rib of beef, 3 lb. 5 oz. @ 1s. 10d. per lb. . . . . . .

6. A customer asked a grocer for 1 lb. of cheese at 1s. 9d. a lb. After cutting off a piece and weighing it, the grocer said " It is a little more than 1 lb.; it will be 1s. 11½d." How many ounces more than 1 lb. was it?

7. Calculate the cost of 1 lb. 13 oz. of cod at 1s. 3½d. a pound.

8. What is the cost of a steak of halibut weighing 11 oz. at 3s. 6d. a pound?

9. What should be the charges for the following items from the fishmonger's?

Fillets of Hake,   3 lb. 10 oz. @ 3s. 6d. per lb. . . . . . .
Dover Sole,   2 lb. 5 oz. @ 2s. 3d. per lb. . . . . . .
Steaks of Turbot, 1 lb. 15 oz. @ 3s. 8d. per lb. . . . . . .

10. When plaice was 2s. 4d. per lb. a customer was charged 3s. 4d. What was the weight of the fish she bought?

Overleaf is an illustration of another type of modern weighing-machine. Use the Price Computing Chart for the questions in Exercise XXVI, Part Two.

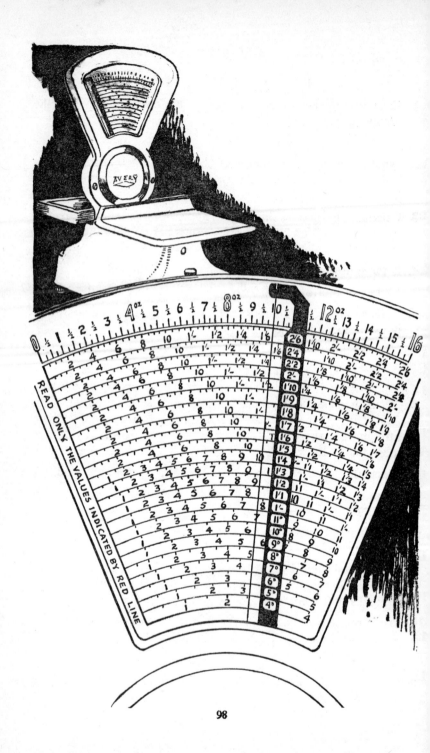

READ ONLY THE VALUES INDICATED BY RED LINE

98

EXERCISE XXVI, Part Two

The following questions are to be done by means of the Price Computing Chart on the opposite page.

In order to use this chart, detached from the weighing-machine, attach a piece of stout drawing paper or thin cardboard underneath page 98 by means of a paper clip so that it extends below the lower edge of the page.

On this drawing paper, produce the zero line and the *red* line on the chart until they intersect in, say, the point *P*. Then the point *P* would be the centre about which, on the actual weighing-machine, the *red* line rotates when goods—sweets, and light groceries—are being weighed.

Example. To find the cost of $7\frac{1}{2}$ ounces of sweets at 2s. 2d. per lb.

Lay a piece of tracing paper over the chart and insert a pin at *P*. Draw a line through *P* to represent the *red* line. Rotate the tracing paper until the line coincides with the $7\frac{1}{2}$-oz. mark on the scale at the top of the chart. The cost—1s.—will be found when the line intersects the band indicating 2s. 2d. per pound.

11. Find the cost of the following weights of sweets at 2s. 4d. per lb.:
   6 oz., $10\frac{1}{2}$ oz., 7 oz., 9 oz., 12 oz., 14 oz., $6\frac{3}{4}$ oz.

12. Find the cost of the following weights of lard at 1s. per lb.:
   5 oz., 9 oz., $7\frac{1}{2}$ oz., $4\frac{3}{4}$ oz., 12 oz., $10\frac{1}{4}$ oz., $8\frac{3}{4}$ oz.

13. Find the cost of the following weights of butter at 1s. 6d. per lb.:
   6 oz., 10 oz., $9\frac{1}{2}$ oz., $12\frac{1}{4}$ oz., 7 oz., 13 oz., $8\frac{1}{2}$ oz.

14. Find the cost of the following weights of bacon at 2s. 6d. per lb.:
   3 oz., 7 oz., 2 oz., 9 oz., $10\frac{1}{2}$ oz., 5 oz., $6\frac{3}{4}$ oz., $12\frac{1}{2}$ oz.

15. Find the cost of the following weights of suet at 2s. per lb.:
   10 oz., 3 oz., 9 oz., 12 oz., $7\frac{1}{2}$ oz., $10\frac{1}{2}$ oz., $13\frac{1}{4}$ oz.

16. Find the cost of the following weights of cheese at 1s. 2d. per lb.:
   6 oz., 4 oz., $7\frac{1}{2}$ oz., $3\frac{1}{2}$ oz., $8\frac{3}{4}$ oz., $10\frac{1}{4}$ oz., $12\frac{3}{4}$ oz.

17. Find the cost of the following weights of dates at 1s. 1d. per lb.:
   2 oz., $5\frac{1}{2}$ oz., $3\frac{1}{4}$ oz., 6 oz., 9 oz., 13 oz., $7\frac{3}{4}$ oz., $9\frac{1}{2}$ oz.

18. Find the cost of the following weights of sweets at 2s. 6d. per lb.
   3 oz., 5 oz., $4\frac{1}{2}$ oz., 7 oz., $8\frac{1}{2}$ oz., 13 oz., 9 oz., 12 oz.

Fig. 3

Weighing in the kitchen

The best kind of weighing-machine for use in the home or in the domestic science room at school is the " dial " pattern (Fig. 3).

Here is a recipe for a currant cake:

Ingredients.

1 lb. flour	2 eggs (beaten)
½ lb. currants	2 teaspoonfuls treacle
¼ lb. sugar	1 teaspoonful mixed spice
¼ lb. butter or lard	1 teaspoonful carbonate of soda
¼ teaspoonful salt	½ pint milk.

There should be no difficulty in weighing out all the solid ingredients needed for this cake, but could we estimate the weight of the cake when baked? We should need to know the weight of an egg; the weight of the milk; (we may neglect the small quantities of the other ingredients): and how much the mixture loses during baking.

When making bread, a baker uses 36 ounces of dough for every 2-lb. loaf. Therefore dough—and cake mixture—loses one-ninth of its weight during the baking process. Let us set this down clearly.

Weight of dough or cake mixture before baking	Weight of baked loaf or cake	Loss during baking
36 ounces	32 ounces	4 ounces

We now see that the loss during baking=one-ninth of the dough or, one-eighth of the baked loaf or cake.

Eggs vary in weight, so we should find the *average* weight of a number of eggs. To do this take, say, half a dozen eggs, and weigh them. We shall find that they weigh about 12 ounces. The average weight of an egg may therefore be taken to be about two ounces.

How shall we find the weight of a pint of milk?

Put a pint of milk in a bottle on the scales; you will find that together, milk and bottle weigh 2 lb. 6 oz. Then empty the milk into a jug, and weigh the empty bottle; you will find that it weighs about 1 lb. 1 oz. Evidently, then, the pint of milk must weigh 1 lb. 5 oz.

The total weight of the ingredients (neglecting the small quantities of salt, treacle, carbonate of soda, and mixed spice) is

Flour	1 lb.
Currants	8 oz.
Sugar	4 oz.
Butter or lard	4 oz.
2 Eggs	4 oz.
$\frac{1}{2}$ pint of milk	10$\frac{1}{2}$ oz.
Total weight	2 lb. 14$\frac{1}{2}$ oz.

The cake mixture loses one-ninth of its weight in baking. One-ninth of 2 lb. 14$\frac{1}{2}$ oz. = one-ninth of 46$\frac{1}{2}$ oz.;
$$= 5\tfrac{1}{4} \text{ oz. (approx.).}$$

Therefore, the weight of the cake when baked should be about 2 lb. 9$\frac{1}{4}$ oz.; which is just over 2$\frac{1}{2}$ lb.

Make a list of the quantities of the ingredients needed to make a cake from the recipe, weighing about 7$\frac{1}{2}$ pounds when baked.

When needed in the recipes in Exercise XXVII, use these values:

1 pint of water weighs 1 lb. 4 oz.
1 pint of milk weighs 1 lb. 5 oz.
4 tea-cupfuls measure 1 pint.
1 tea-cupful of sugar weighs 6 oz.
1 tea-cupful of flour weighs 3$\frac{1}{2}$ oz.
1 tea-cupful of oatmeal weighs 2 oz.
1 tea-cupful of treacle weighs 9 oz.
1 egg (average) weighs 2 oz.

EXERCISE XXVII

Calculate the weight, before and after baking, of the ingredients, except baking-powder, spice, etc., in each of the following recipes.

1. Ginger Bread.

$\frac{1}{4}$ lb. flour   1 oz. butter
1 oz. sugar   1 egg
$\frac{1}{2}$ oz. lemon peel $\frac{1}{2}$ oz. cherries
1 teaspoonful ground ginger   tea-cupful of milk
1 teaspoonful soda $\frac{1}{2}$ tea-cupful treacle

2. Parkin.

$2\frac{1}{2}$ tea-cupfuls flour   1 teaspoonful ground ginger
2 tea-cupfuls oatmeal   1 teaspoonful cinnamon
1 tea-cupful brown sugar   2 teaspoonfuls mixed spice
$\frac{1}{4}$ lb. melted lard   1 tea-cupful treacle
$1\frac{1}{2}$ teaspoonfuls bicarbonate of soda   1 egg

3. Simnel Cake.

$\frac{1}{2}$ lb. flour $\frac{1}{2}$ lb. currants
$\frac{1}{2}$ lb. castor sugar   1 nutmeg
$\frac{1}{2}$ lb. butter $\frac{1}{4}$ lb. lemon peel
Pinch of salt   4 eggs

4. Christmas Cake.

$\frac{1}{2}$ lb. castor sugar $\frac{1}{2}$ lb. butter
10 oz. plain flour   1 teaspoonful baking powder
$1\frac{1}{2}$ lb. currants   Pinch salt
$\frac{1}{4}$ lb. candied peel $\frac{1}{4}$ lb. ground almonds
                5 eggs

5. Calculate the cost of the ingredients in this Christmas Cake and the cost per pound of the baked cake, based on the following prices:

Castor Sugar	5d. per lb.
Flour	3d. per lb.
Currants	10d. per lb.
Candied Peel	5s. per lb.
Butter	1s. 4d. per lb.
Ground Almonds	2s. 8d. per lb.
Eggs	3d. each

Weighing baby

The first few weeks of a baby's life are most important. In order to find out whether the child is getting the right sort of food, mother should weigh baby at regular intervals, say, once a week.

From the chemist's she can get a chart on which to record baby's weight, week by week, in spaces provided; mother can then see if baby is making normal progress, by comparing its weight with the average weight of babies of the same age shown in the chart. A gain of 4 ounces to 6 ounces per week is an indication of healthy development.

WEEKLY RECORD OF BABY'S WEIGHT

	lb.	oz.	Average weight of babies of same age lb.	oz.		lb.	oz.	Average weight of babies of same age lb.	oz.
At Birth			7	0	At 14 weeks			11	12
„ 1 week			7	4	„ 15 weeks			12	2
„ 2 weeks			7	8	„ 16 weeks			12	8
„ 3 weeks			7	12	„ 17 weeks			12	14
„ 4 weeks			8	0	„ 18 weeks			13	4
„ 5 weeks			8	6	„ 19 weeks			13	10
„ 6 weeks			8	12	„ 20 weeks			14	0
„ 7 weeks			9	2	„ 21 weeks			14	6
„ 8 weeks			9	8	„ 22 weeks			14	12
„ 9 weeks			9	12	„ 23 weeks			15	2
„ 10 weeks			10	0	„ 24 weeks			15	8
„ 11 weeks			10	8	„ 25 weeks			15	13
„ 12 weeks			11	0	„ 26 weeks			16	2
„ 13 weeks			11	6	„ 27 weeks			16	7

A Pictorial Record Chart of Baby's Weight is interesting, and easy to keep and to understand. Such charts can be got from the chemist, or one may be made out of paper ruled in, say, quarter-inch squares.

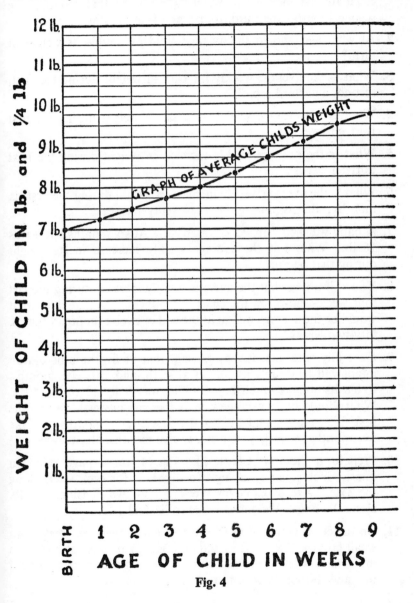

Fig. 4

EXERCISE XXVIII

1. From the weights given in the " averages " column, on page 104, calculate the increase in weight during the first month; the second month; the third, fourth and fifth months.

2. At what age, should the average child be double its weight at birth?

3. What is the average weekly increase in weight during the first, second, and third months?

4. What is the average weekly increase in weight during the first thirteen weeks?

5. What is the average weekly increase in weight during the next thirteen weeks?

6. What is the average weekly increase in weight during the first six months; that is, during the first twenty-six weeks?

7. A baby weighed 7 lb. 12 oz. at birth. At six months old it was 16 lb. What was the average weekly increase in its weight during that period?

8. You will notice that the average weekly increase during the last four weeks shown on the chart is 5 ounces. At that rate, what would be the average weight at the end of twelve months: that is, fifty-two weeks?

9. Generally speaking, it may be said that at five months old an infant will be double its weight at birth, and at twelve months, treble its weight at birth. A child was 8 lb. 12 oz. at birth. What should be its average weekly increase in weight during the first five months, and during the first twelve months? (Take five months to be 20 weeks and twelve months, fifty-two weeks.)

10. Prepare a Pictorial Chart, like Fig. 4, on a page ruled in quarter-inch squares, taking two divisions for each week along the *axis* " Age of Child in Weeks " and two divisions per lb. along the *axis* " Weight of Child in lb. and $\frac{1}{4}$-lb."

11. On the chart prepared in Question 8 mark, week by week, with small crosses, " x ", the weight of a baby, 7 lb. 4 oz. at birth, the increase in weight per week during the first four weeks being 4 oz., and during the second four weeks 5 oz.

EXERCISE XXIX

THE AVERAGE WEIGHT OF A HEALTHY BOY OR GIRL
(WHEN DRESSED)

Age	Boys	Girls
	St. Lb.	St. Lb.
1 year	1 7	1 6
2 years	1 13	1 12
3 years	2 3	2 2
4 years	2 7	2 6
5 years	2 13	2 12
6 years	3 3	3 2
7 years	3 8	3 6
8 years	3 13	3 11
9 years	4 4	4 2
10 years	4 11	4 8
11 years	5 2	5 0
12 years	5 10	5 12
13 years	6 4	6 8

Note. In the above table, weights are given in stones and pounds. A stone = 14 pounds.

In some weighing machines, such as are used in schools and in clinics, the weights are recorded only in pounds.

1. Make a table showing the Average Weight in pounds of Healthy Boys and Girls for the age range in the table above.

2. What is the average increase per month in the weight of:
   (*a*) boys, (*b*) girls, during their sixth year?

3. On a sheet of paper ruled in 10 divisions to the inch (this paper is called *graph* paper) prepare a chart like Fig. 5 overleaf, taking 5 divisions along the axis which runs from left to right to represent an interval of one year, and 5 divisions along the axis at right-angles to this axis to represent 10 lb. weight.

4. On the chart which you prepared for Question 3 draw a graph showing the growth in weight of Healthy Boys from birth to the age of 13 years, using the weights in lb.

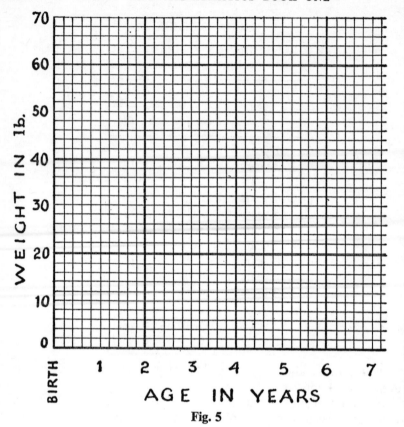

Fig. 5

5. On the same chart draw a graph showing the growth in weight of Healthy Girls from birth to the age of 13 years.

6. What information do we get from the graphs for boys, and girls, between the ages of 11 and 12 years.

7. From your graphs estimate the weight of the average girl at the following ages:

> 11 years 3 months;
> 12 years 2 months;
> 9 years 7 months.

8. From your graphs, estimate the approximate age of the average girls of the following weights:

> 45 lb.,   4 st. 6 lb.,   50 lb.,   86 lb.

9. The ages and weights of three sisters are shown below:

Ages	Weights
8 years 6 months	4 st.
10 years 2 months	4 st. 9 lb.
11 years 10 months	5 st. 9 lb.

By means of your graphs, estimate the amount, above or below the average for her age, of each of the sisters.

10. Four boys in a team for a relay swimming race for 13-year olds weighed respectively:

6 st. 8 lb., 7 st. 1 lb., 6 st. 10 lb., 6 st. 9 lb.

Calculate their average weight.

11. Here are the weights of the members of the crews in the Boat Race in a certain year, when Cambridge won.

Cambridge	Oxford
1. 11 st. 2 lb. (Bow)	1. 11 st. $9\frac{1}{2}$ lb. (Bow)
2. 12 st. 4 lb.	2. 11 st. 1 lb.
3. 13 st.	3. 12 st. 12 lb.
4. 13 st. 3 lb.	4. 14 st.
5. 13 st. 7 lb.	5. 12 st. $11\frac{1}{2}$ lb.
6. 13 st. 8 lb.	6. 12 st. $10\frac{1}{2}$ lb.
7. 13 st. 1 lb.	7. 12 st. $12\frac{1}{2}$ lb.
8. 12 st. $4\frac{1}{2}$ lb.	8. 12 st. 13 lb.
8 st. 9 lb. (Cox)	9 st. 3 lb. (Cox)

Calculate the total weight of each crew, (a) excluding the Cox, (b) including the Cox.

12. Compare the total weights of the two crews in (a) the front half of the boats, that is, numbers 1 to 4 inclusive, (b) in the rear half, including the cox.

13. Calculate the average weight of the lightest four members of each of the Oxford and Cambridge crews, including the cox in each boat.

14. Calculate the average weight of the heaviest four members of each of the Oxford and Cambridge crews.

Transport by road and rail

If you examine a railway waggon, you will find, somewhere on it, the word " TARE " followed by some numbers;   for instance,

	tons	cwts.	qrs.
Tare	2	3	3

What does this mean?

Before we answer this question, let us see how a coal merchant finds how much coal there is in a waggon that has come from the coalpit. Do you remember how we found the weight of a pint of milk? We weighed a pint of milk in a bottle, then we weighed the empty bottle, and by subtraction we got the weight of the milk.   In the same way, the weight of coal in a waggon is found.   The waggon loaded with coal is weighed, and from it the weight of the empty waggon, which is called the " tare of the waggon " is subtracted.   This gives the weight of the coal in the waggon.

Find the weight of the coal in the waggon from these particulars.

		tons	cwts.	qrs.
" Gross weight ", that is, weight of waggon and coal	=	9	14	2
Tare of waggon	=	2	3	3
" Net weight " of coal	=	7	10	3

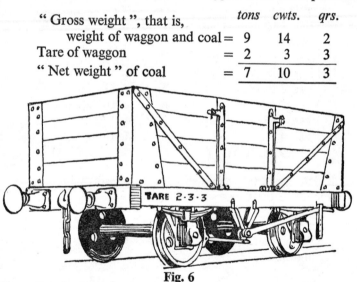

Fig. 6

This is how the tare of a vehicle is found.   The vehicle is driven on to the plate of a large weighing machine.   The man in the building shown in Fig. 7 operates the machine, just as the school nurse operates the school weighing-machine. The weight of the unloaded vehicle is its tare.

The tare is marked on a railway waggon before it leaves the works.

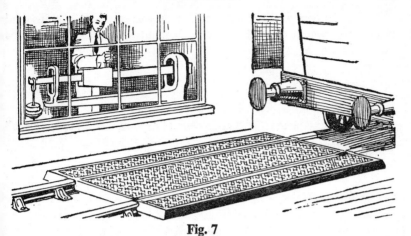

Fig. 7

On motor coaches, and on single- and double-decker buses, instead of the word tare, the block letters, U. W., followed by numbers, and sometimes a statement about the seating capacity of the vehicle are to be seen (Fig. 8).

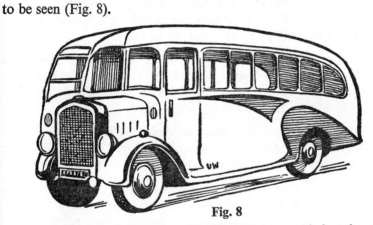

Fig. 8

For instance, on a Blackpool double-decker bus this is painted:

	T.	C.	Q.
U. W.	7	4	3
Seating Capacity		48	

U. W. stands for Unloaded Weight, which, in this case, is 7 tons 4 cwts. 3 qrs.

The unloaded weight of an average 32-seater long-distance motor coach is about 6 tons 10 cwts., that is, $6\frac{1}{2}$ tons.

In the following advertisement for motor commercial vans and trucks, the weight quoted refers to the loads of goods that may be safely carried in each.

" Commercial Vehicles Limited.

The following vehicles are offered, second-hand, at reasonable prices:

Vans and trucks: 8 cwts., 25 cwts., 2/3 tons, 4/5 tons, 6/8 tons."

The statements, 2/3 tons, 4/5 tons, etc., mean in this and similar advertisements, from 2 to 3 tons; from 4 to 5 tons; and so on.

These facts should be borne in mind when you are working the questions in Exercise XXX.

EXERCISE XXX

1. Do you know the following useful facts? If you don't, find them in a book of tables and memorise them:

    (*a*) The number of lb. in 1 cwt.; in 1 ton; in 1 quarter.
        (*Note :* a *quarter* means one-quarter of a hundredweight.)
    (*b*) The number of hundredweights in 1 ton.

2. The tare of a railway hand-truck was 8 cwts. 2 qrs. When loaded with a passenger's luggage it weighed 10 cwts. The passenger had to pay 1d. for every lb. of luggage over 112 lb. which is allowed free. How much had he to pay?

3. The gross weight of a waggon loaded with coal was 9 tons 16 cwts. The tare of the waggon was 1 ton 17 cwts. Calculate the weight of coal in the waggon.

4. Here are the particulars relating to four waggon loads of coal delivered to a coal merchant at the coal wharf:

	Gross Weight			Tare		
	T.	*C.*	*Q.*	*T.*	*C.*	*Q.*
I.	11	2	1	2	3	3
II.	9	18	3	1	16	–
III.	10	5	2	2	1	3
IV.	8	17	–	1	19	2

How much coal was delivered to him?

5. Calculate the average weight of coal per truck in Question 4.

6. A lorry loaded with coke weighed 2 tons 18 cwts. The tare of the lorry was 19 cwts. What was the weight of coke on it?

7. The unloaded weight of a lorry was 1 ton 7½ cwts. 800 bricks, each weighing 8¼ lb., were loaded on to it. Calculate the gross weight of the lorry and bricks.

8. Calculate the greatest number of pressed bricks, each weighing 9 lb., that can be safely loaded on a 4-ton truck.

9. Calculate the greatest number of cubic feet of oak, the density of which is 50 lb. per cubic foot, that may be safely loaded on a 10-ton motor lorry.

10. The inscription on a 32-seater motor coach was

	T.	C.	Q.
U.W.	6	13	1

On a tour it came to a temporary bridge over a river, bearing the notice:

" Maximum load permitted to go over the bridge, 8½ tons."

If the coach were full, the average weight of the passengers being 10 st., could the coach safely cross the bridge?

11. Reckoning the weight of passengers to be on an average 10 st. 3 lb., what would be the loaded weight of a full double-decker bus that bore the inscription:

	T.	C.	Q.	
U.W.	7	5	–	Seating Capacity 53

12. The unloaded weight of a lorry was 18 cwts. When loaded with logs its gross weight was 2 tons 5 cwts. Calculate the weight of the logs.

13. The gross weight of a waggon loaded with tarmacadam was 5 tons 7 cwts. The tare of the waggon was 1 ton 16 cwts. Calculate the weight of the tarmacadam.

14. The tare of a railway porter's truck was 3 cwts. 2 qrs. When loaded with a passenger's luggage its gross weight was 5 cwts. 1 qr. Calculate (a) the total weight of the luggage, (b) the excess over 112 lbs. allowed free.

15. The unloaded weight of a small motor car was 17 cwts. 3 qrs. Calculate the gross weight of the vehicle when the weight of the driver was 10 st. 12 lbs. and 2 passengers, 9 st. 3 lb., 6 st. 13 lb respectively.

VI

TIME AND THE CALENDAR

Measuring time

I wonder if it has ever occurred to you as strange that all our
divisions of time—except the week—are multiples of the number six.
First, we have the " four-and-twenty blackbirds baked in a pie ":
that is, the twenty-four hours in a day: a division handed down to
us from very ancient times. The Babylonians, many centuries before
the birth of Christ, reckoned twenty-four hours to the day. The
Hebrews divided these twenty-four hours into two groups of twelve:
twelve from sunrise to sunset, and twelve from sunset to sunrise.
When we read, in the New Testament, that during the Crucifixion of
Christ, " It was about the sixth hour, and there was darkness over
all the earth until the ninth hour ", we are to understand that
these hours were the sixth to the ninth after sunrise. Now about
Easter time the sun rises about six o'clock in the morning by our
time, so from the sixth to the ninth hour of the Hebrew way of
reckoning would be the same as from noon to three o'clock by our
time.

Then, we have twelve months in the year, and sixty minutes in an
hour, and sixty seconds in a minute: all divisions that are multiples
of the number six.

Now, why did these ancient peoples base all their divisions of time
on the number six?

Most boys and girls when first they play with a pair of compasses
find out how to draw a six-pointed star-like figure like this:

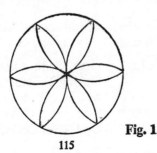

Fig. 1

That is, they learn—without knowing it—a very important fact about a circle: that it can be easily divided to six parts. The Egyptians and the Greeks knew this fact, and they made it the basis of their reckoning. This is what they did. They divided each of the six large divisions—into which a circle was divided—into ten smaller divisions—ten was probably chosen because there are ten fingers on our hands—thus making sixty divisions altogether in the complete circle. Sixty, therefore, became their system of counting. They had not numbers, such as 1, 2, 3, and so on—those were invented later by the Arabs—they used the letters of their alphabets to represent numbers. Where we have ten numbers, they had sixty! What a difficult job it must have been in those days, you will say, to do sums. It was, but not quite so difficult as we imagine it to be.

When the Egyptians wanted to write, say, the number sixty-four, that is one sixty, and four extra, they wrote first the letter corresponding to 1, and after it, the letter corresponding to 4. We shall use our Arabic numerals to write this. The number sixty-four would then be

$$1 \quad 4.$$

The number one hundred and twenty-one would be written

$$2 \quad 1,$$

which means 2 sixties, that is 120, and 1. To add these two numbers together as the Egyptians and the Greeks would have done it we should get

$$3 \quad 5,$$

which means 3 sixties and 5. Now, this is not so strange as it may seem, for we do something like this ourselves at the present time; every time we write down the time of departure or arrival of a train which we find in a railway time-table, or the time of a broadcast programme.

Here, for instance, are some particulars relating to Broadcasts for Schools on a certain day:

10 5 to 10 15	News Commentary for Schools.
11 0 to 11 20	Singing Together.
11 20 to 11 40	Music and Movement for Juniors.
2 5 to 2 30	Stories from World History.
2 30 to 3 15	Orchestral Concert for Schools.

Suppose we wish to know how long the Orchestral Concert lasts; we should have to do a subtraction sum.   Here it is:

$$3 \ 15$$
$$\underline{2 \ 30}$$
$$\overline{\hphantom{2 \ 30}}$$

We say, " 30 minutes from 15 minutes ".   We cannot take 30 from 15, so we take one of the hours, and turn it into minutes: that is, 60 minutes; then 30 minutes from 60 minutes leaves 30 minutes, to which we add the 15 minutes and we get 45 minutes as the length of the concert.

Thus our system of measuring time, and of adding and subtracting amounts of time is a relic of the methods used by the Greeks, the Egyptians and Babylonians centuries before the birth of Christ.

EXERCISE XXXI

From the Broadcasting Time-table on page 116, find:

1. The length in minutes of each of the broadcasts.

2. The number of minutes of School Broadcasts in the morning.

3. The number of hours and minutes of School Broadcasting on that day.

4. A Children's Hour broadcast started at 5 o'clock and ended at five minutes to six.   How long did it last?

5. Broadcasting started, on a certain day, at 7.55 a.m., and ended at 11.03 p.m.   How many hours and minutes of broadcasting were there on that day?

6. A boy lived 12 minutes walk from school.   At what time should he leave home so as to arrive at school five minutes before the School Assembly at 9.05 a.m.?

7. A concert lasted from 7.45 p.m. to 10.30 p.m.   How long did it last?

8. A variety broadcast started at 8.25 p.m. and ended at 10.0 p.m. How long did it last?

9. A workman started a job at 8.30 a.m. and finished it at 4.15 p.m. He had 1 hour off for dinner.   How long did the job take?

DAY	9.5 TO 9.40	9.40 TO 10.5	10.5 TO 10.45	10.45 TO 11.0	11.0 TO 11.30	11.30 TO NOON	1.30 TO 2.15	2.15 TO 2.55	2.55 TO 3.5	3.5 TO 3.50
MONDAY	Assembly & Religious Instruction	Physical Training	Arts and Crafts	Recreation	Arts and Crafts		Maths	Hist.	Recreation	Music
TUESDAY			Maths.		English		Hist.	Prep.		Drawing
WEDNESDAY			English		Science		Maths.	Geog.		Music
THURSDAY			Maths.		English	Music	Handicraft			Drawing
FRIDAY			Music		Geog.	Maths.	Science			Prep.

Fig. 2

Fig. 2 is a copy of a School Time-table to be used in connection with Questions 7 to 10.

10. How many hours and minutes are spent in school in the mornings and in the afternoons.

11. How much time, each day, is spent in recreation.

12. How much time, each day, is spent in lessons and other activities.

13. How much time, each week, is devoted to each of the following activities and lessons:

(a) Assembly and Religious Instruction.
(b) Physical Training.
(c) Music.
(d) English.
(e) Geography.
(f) History.
(g) Mathematics.
(h) Science.
(i) Drawing.
(j) Arts and Crafts.

RAILWAY TIME-TABLES

(Unofficial Abridged Schedules)

(*Note.* The times given in the following unofficial abridged schedules are only approximate. For correct times, consult the current official time-tables.)

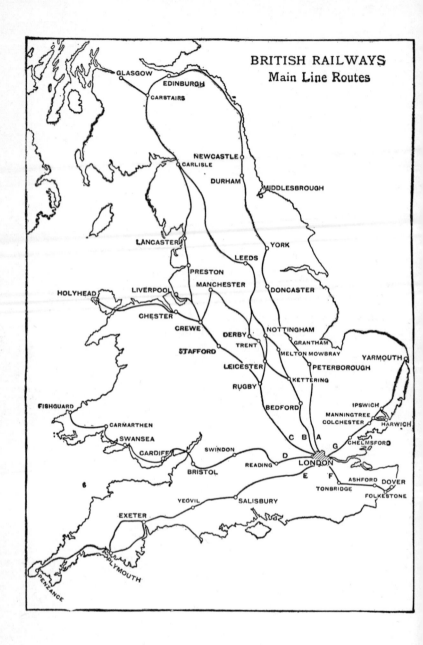

BRITISH RAILWAYS
Main Line Routes

GLASGOW
EDINBURGH
CARSTAIRS
NEWCASTLE
CARLISLE
DURHAM
MIDDLESBROUGH
LANCASTER
YORK
LEEDS
PRESTON
MANCHESTER
HOLYHEAD
LIVERPOOL
DONCASTER
CHESTER
CREWE
DERBY
NOTTINGHAM
TRENT
GRANTHAM
STAFFORD
MELTON MOWBRAY
YARMOUTH
LEICESTER
PETERBOROUGH
RUGBY
KETTERING
FISHGUARD
BEDFORD
IPSWICH
MANNINGTREE
CARMARTHEN
COLCHESTER
HARWICH
SWANSEA
C B A
CARDIFF
SWINDON
CHELMSFORD
D
G
READING
LONDON
BRISTOL
E F
YEOVIL
ASHFORD DOVER
SALISBURY
TONBRIDGE
FOLKESTONE
EXETER
PENZANCE
PLYMOUTH

120

INDEX TO STATIONS

Name of Station	Route	Name of Station	Route
Ashford (Kent)	F	Leeds	B
		Leicester	B
Bristol	D	Liverpool	C
		Liverpool Street (London)	G
Cannon St. (London)	F	London Bridge (London)	F
Cardiff	D		
Carlisle	B & C	Manchester	B & C
Carmarthen	D		
Charing Cross (London)	F	Newcastle-on-Tyne	A
Chelmsford	G	Nottingham	B
Colchester	G		
Crewe	C	Paddington (London)	D
		Peterborough	A
Derby	B	Plymouth	E
Dover	F	Preston	C
Edinburgh	A, B & C	Reading	D
Euston (London)	C	Rugby	C
Exeter	E		
		St. Pancras (London)	B
Fishguard	D	Salisbury	E
		Stafford	C
Glasgow	C	Swansea	D
Grantham	A	Swindon	D
Harwich	G	Tonbridge	F
Holyhead	C		
		Waterloo (London)	E
Ipswich	G		
		Yarmouth	G
King's Cross (London)	A	Yeovil	E
		York	A

	a.m.	a.m. (FLYING SCOTSMAN)	p.m.
Edinburgh	—	10 0	7 50
Newcastle	6 0	12 43	11 17
York	9 30	2 20	1 20
Grantham	—	3 57	3 32
Peterborough	11 46	—	4 19
King's Cross	1 25	6 5	6 5

	a.m.	a.m.	p.m.
Edinburgh	—	10 10	—
Carlisle	—	1 1	—
Leeds	—	3 43	—
Derby	—	—	—
Manchester	7 52	—	12 16
Derby	8 55	—	2 21
Trent	—	—	—
Nottingham	—	6 0	—
Trent	—	—	—
Leicester	9 36	—	3 20
Kettering	—	7 24	4 10
St. Pancras	11 50	9 15	6 45

ROUTE A

		a.m.	p.m.	p.m.
—	King's Cross	9 30	1 0	7 0
76	Peterborough	—	2 28	—
105	Grantham	11 38	—	9 22
188	York	1 14	4 46	10 47
268	Newcastle	3 7	6 35	12 38
393	Edinburgh	5 49	9 32	3 23

ROUTE B

		a.m.	a.m.	p.m.
—	St. Pancras a.	8 15	8 55	12 ngt
72	Kettering	9 50	10 21	1 59
99	Leicester	10 33	—	2 47
120	Trent a.	—	—	3 21
123	Nottingham d.	—	11 30	—
120	Trent d.	11 22	—	3 24
128	Derby a.	—	—	3 41
190	Manchester d.	1 15	—	—
128	Derby d.	—	—	3 53
197	Leeds	—	1 45	6 36
311	Carlisle	—	—	—
409	Edinburgh	—	7 19	—

ROUTE C

		a.m.	a.m.	p.m.
—	Euston	8 30	10 0	9 25
83	Rugby	10 9	11 53	11 15
134	Stafford	—	—	12 37
158	Crewe a.	11 49	1 7	1 17
194	Liverpool	12 55	—	—
187	Manchester	1 0	—	—
264	Holyhead	4 49	—	2 23
158	Crewe d.	12 8	1 15	1 29
209	Preston	1 29	—	—
290	Carlisle	—	4 18	—
400	Edinburgh	—	7 45	8 0
402	Glasgow	—	6 50	7 45

	a.m.	p.m.	p.m.
Glasgow	10 30	1 0	5 40
Edinburgh	10 30	1 15	5 35
Carlisle	1 15	3 52	8 35
Preston	3 38	—	—
Crewe a.	5 11	6 51	12 50
Holyhead	—	2 35	—
Manchester	—	5 35	—
Liverpool	—	5 40	—
Crewe d.	5 20	7 10	1 10
Stafford	5 54	—	—
Rugby	7 6	—	2 53
Euston	8 50	10 0	5 20

ROUTE D

		a.m.	a.m.	p.m.
—	Paddington	—	11 35	1 55
36	Reading	—	—	2 42
78	Swindon	—	—	3 35
118	Bristol	9 42	2 35	—
146	Cardiff	11 0	3 55	5 20
191	Swansea	1 5	4 50	6 56
220	Carmarthen	2 23	6 0	8 4
261	Fishguard	—	—	—

	a.m.	a.m.	p.m.
Fishguard	3 35	—	—
Carmarthen	—	7 30	8 32
Swansea	—	8 50	9 28
Cardiff	7 0	10 10	11 0
Bristol	—	11 15	—
Swindon	—	1 7	2 12
Reading	—	2 20	3 21
Paddington	10 30	2 40	4 20

		a.m.	a.m.	p.m.
Plymouth		8 15	10 0	3 45
Exeter		10 23	12 17	5 45
Yeovil		—	1 40	7 8
Salisbury		12 36	2 44	8 9
Waterloo		2 29	4 41	10 27

	a.m.	a.m.	p.m.
Dover	8 56	11 52	3 50
Ashford	9 47	12 40	4 49
Tonbridge	10 28	1 21	5 27
London Bridge	11 23	2 14	6 47
Cannon Street	—	—	6 58
Waterloo	11 30	2 22	—
Charing Cross	11 34	2 28	—

	a.m.	a.m.	p.m.
Yarmouth	8 0	9 0	2 40
Ipswich	9 46	11 28	5 0
Manningtree a.	—	11 44	—
Harwich	—	10 55	—
Manningtree d.	—	11 46	—
Colchester	—	12 8	5 30
Chelmsford	—	12 46	6 4
Liverpool St.	11 28	1 38	6 52

ROUTE E

		a.m.	a.m.	p.m.
—	Waterloo	9 0	10 50	2 50
83	Salisbury	11 5	12 33	4 42
124	Yeovil	12 6	—	—
171	Exeter	1 24	2 29	6 46
234	Plymouth	3 47	4 55	9 14

ROUTE F

		a.m.	a.m.	p.m.
—	Charing Cross	—	9 15	1 15
—	Waterloo	—	9 17	1 17
—	Cannon Street	7 34	—	—
—	London Bridge	7 27	—	—
31	Tonbridge	8 48	10 3	—
56	Ashford	9 33	10 35	2 24
77	Dover	10 21	11 21	3 5

ROUTE G

		a.m.	p.m.	p.m.
—	Liverpool St.	8 12	12 30	4 5
30	Chelmsford	9 4	—	4 52
52	Colchester	9 37	—	5 28
60	Manningtree a.	—	—	5 48
69	Harwich	—	—	6 28
60	Manningtree d.	10 4	2 1	5 51
69	Ipswich	1 2	4 5	6 10
122	Yarmouth	—	—	8 10

How to read a railway time-table

The Time-tables A to G on pages 122 to 124 are abridged time-tables, that is, they contain only a selection of trains and important stations.

The following study of them will help us to understand the official time-tables of British Railways, which are issued for different sections of the system, and the still more comprehensive time-tables, familiarly known as *Bradshaws*.

The simplest of the abridged time-tables are those for Routes A, D, E and F. We shall find that these present no difficulty; those for Routes B, C and G need a little explanation: this will be given presently.

Find the time of a morning train from Bristol to Carmarthen.

First look up either Bristol or Carmarthen in the Index to Stations on page 121. There you will find that these places are on Route D.

Next turn to Route D and you will find the route from Bristol to Carmarthen in the left-hand part of the table.

The only morning train shown leaves Bristol at 9.42 a.m. and reaches Carmarthen at 2.23: this will be 2.23 p.m. although it occurs in the column headed a.m.

How long does the 9.42 a.m. train from Bristol take to reach Carmarthen?

It reaches Carmarthen at	2 .	23 p.m.
It left Bristol at	9 .	42 a.m.
Time for the journey is		4 hrs. 41 mins.

How many miles is it from Bristol to Carmarthen?

In the column on the extreme left of the table are the distances from London of the towns named.

London to Carmarthen = 220 miles
London to Bristol   = 118 miles

Therefore,   Bristol to Carmarthen = 102 miles

Calculate the average speed of the 9.42 a.m. train from Bristol to Carmarthen.

The train travels 102 miles in 4 hrs. 41 mins.;
that is, it travels   102 miles in 281 minutes.

Therefore, it travels, on an average, $\frac{60}{281}$ of 102 miles in an hour;

that is, $\dfrac{6120}{281}$ miles per hour.

$$
\begin{array}{r}
21 \\
281\,\overline{\smash{)}\,6120} \\
562 \\
\hline
500 \\
281 \\
\hline
219 \\
\end{array}
$$

that is, nearly 22 miles per hour.

Now examine Route C. You will notice that Crewe occurs twice in the table, and between the two entries there are two parallel lines across the table enclosing the towns,

> Liverpool,
> Manchester,
> Holyhead.

Look at the map on page 120. On Route C, at Crewe branch lines radiate, one to Liverpool and Preston, one to Manchester, and another to Holyhead. Crewe, therefore, is a junction.

The 8.30 a.m. train from Euston arrives at Crewe at 11.49 a.m. Passengers on it who wish to go to Liverpool, Manchester or Holyhead, have to change at Crewe. To allow them to do so the train waits there from 11.49 a.m. until 12.8 p.m. when it departs for Preston, which is on the main line.

The time-table does not show how long the passengers who had to change have to wait for the trains for Liverpool, Manchester and Holyhead; usually their trains are already in Crewe station ready to start as soon as the main line train has left.

In the same way, the time-table at the right of Route C shows that passengers from Liverpool, Manchester and Holyhead can join the train from Glasgow and Edinburgh to London at Crewe.

Route B is still a little more complicated. It has to serve passengers from London to the midland towns of Leicester, Derby and Nottingham; the towns in the West Riding of Yorkshire, and Manchester.

Consider the journey from London to Leeds.

Just north of Kettering the line divides into two branches. One branch passes through Melton Mowbray and Nottingham, the other goes through Leicester and Derby.

The 8.55 a.m. from St. Pancras takes the former route, passing through Kettering at 10.21 a.m., and Nottingham at 11.30 a.m., arriving at Leeds at 1.45 p.m.

The midnight train takes the latter route, passing through Leicester at 2.47 a.m., Derby at 3.41 a.m., and arrives at Leeds at 6.36 a.m.

The main line goes through Derby, so the Melton Mowbray portion is the branch line to Nottingham. That is why Nottingham is printed between two parallel lines in the time-table. The line from Derby to Manchester, too, is a branch line, so Manchester is shown in the time-table between two parallel lines.

In Route G we see there is a branch line about 9 miles long, from Manningtree to Harwich, the part for the Harwich-Hook of Holland route to the Continent.

EXERCISE XXXII

1. How long does it take the Flying Scotsman to reach London from Edinburgh?

2. How many miles is it from Edinburgh to London?

3. Calculate the average speed of the Flying Scotsman, in miles per hour, between Edinburgh and London.

4. Calculate, in hours and minutes, the length of the journey from King's Cross to Edinburgh by each of the three trains shown in the table, Route A.

5. Calculate the average speed between King's Cross and Grantham, of (a) the 9.30 a.m., (b) the 7.0 p.m.

6. Compare the time to reach London from Edinburgh by the 10.10 a.m. on Route B, with that of the Flying Scotsman.

7. Compare the average speed in miles per hour of the 10.10 a.m. Edinburgh to St. Pancras, with the speed of the Flying Scotsman found in Question 3.

8. Which train takes the longer time to reach St. Pancras from Manchester, the 7.52 a.m. or the 12.16 p.m.? What is the difference?

9. Which of the three trains from Edinburgh, the 10.30 a.m., the 1.15 p.m., and the 5.35 p.m., take the longest time to reach Euston, and which takes the least time? How do these times compare with the time taken by the Flying Scotsman?

10. By calculating the times between Waterloo and Plymouth for each of the three trains shown in the time-table, show that the 10.50 a.m. is the fastest, and the 9.0 a.m. the slowest of the three.

11. How many miles is it from London to Plymouth?

12. Calculate the average speed of the 10.50 a.m. Waterloo to Plymouth on its complete run, and compare this with the speed of the Flying Scotsman.

13. How many miles is it from Harwich to Liverpool Street?

14. Calculate the average speed of the Harwich to Liverpool Street boat train, that is, the 10.55 a.m., on its complete run.

15. Calculate the average speed of the Charing Cross to Dover boat train, that is, the 1.15 p.m. from Charing Cross.

16. Calculate the average speed of the Fishguard to Paddington boat train, that is, the 3.35 a.m. from Fishguard, on its complete run. Compare this with the speed of the Flying Scotsman found in Question 3.

17. Find the times of departure and arrival of the following trains:

    (*a*) morning, from St. Pancras to Nottingham;
    (*b*) morning, from St. Pancras to Leeds.

18. Which route does the morning train from St. Pancras to Leeds take: via Derby, or via Melton Mowbray?

19. Find the times of departure and arrival of trains for the following journeys:

    (*a*) Manchester to Leicester in the morning;
    (*b*) Cardiff to Paddington at night;
    (*c*) Exeter to Waterloo in the morning.

20. Calculate the number of hours and minutes in each of the railway journeys in Question 19.

21. Calculate the average speed of the 10.23 a.m. train from Exeter to Waterloo. How does this compare with the speed of the Flying Scotsman?

22. You are planning a railway journey from Manchester to Dover, to be completed in one day. Write down the time of departure from Manchester; the time of arrival in Dover; and the length of time you may spend in London en route.

23. A passenger returning from the Continent via Hook of Holland arrived in Harwich about breakfast time. He is then to travel to Exeter. Write down the times of departure and arrival of the convenient trains, and state the length of time that he would have to cross London from station to station.

24. Write down the details of times of departure and arrival for a journey from Swindon to Grantham. How much time is available for crossing London from station to station?

25. At what time should a passenger leave Derby in the morning so as to be in Harwich by 6.28 in the evening? How much time would that leave him in London?

26. How much time would a business man be able to spend in Derby by leaving St. Pancras at 8.15 a.m., returning by an afternoon train? How long would the visit take from leaving to returning to St. Pancras?

27. The 7.30 a.m. from Carmarthen to Paddington divides into two portions at Cardiff, one portion reaches Paddington without stop, the other portion stops at Bristol, Swindon and Reading. Calculate the average speeds of these two portions between Cardiff and Paddington, assuming that the express leaves Cardiff at 10.10 a.m., and the other part 5 minutes later.

28. What is the latest time that a passenger should leave Colchester if he is to catch the boat train from Euston to Holyhead, arriving at Holyhead at 2.23 a.m.?

29. At what time, at the latest, should a passenger leave Dover so as to reach York the same day?

30. How long, according to the schedules, would the passenger in Question 29 be in London, between his arrival at Charing Cross and his departure from King's Cross?

The calendar

If you do not already know it, learn the following:

> Thirty days hath September,
> April, June and November;
> All the rest have thirty-one,
> Except February alone,
> Which has but twenty-eight days clear,
> And twenty-nine in a leap year.

As you know, there are twelve months in a year. Only five of them are named in the rhyme, so there must be seven months, each of which contains thirty-one days. If you do not know already how many days there are in a year, you should now be able to reckon them.

How do we tell which years are leap years? Let us take the year 1967. This means 19 centuries and 67 years after Christ was born. The 67 years does not divide exactly by 4; so *that* year is not a leap year. The year 1984 is a leap year because the 84 divides exactly by 4. This gives us the general rule: " Neglect the century, and divide the remaining years by 4. If there is no remainder, then the year is a leap year."

If there is an exact number of centuries in a date, say, 18, 19 or 20 we divide the number of centuries by 4; if there is no remainder, that year is a leap year. The years 1800 and 1900 are not leap years because 18 and 19 do not divide exactly by 4; but the year 2000 is a leap year because 20 is exactly divisible by 4.

Has it ever occurred to you why, in a leap year, the extra day is added at the end of February? Well, it was Julius Caesar who, 45 years before Christ was born, after consulting a very learned Greek astronomer, ordered people to add an extra day to the three hundred and sixty-five, at the end of every fourth year. In his day, and even in England until the year 1752, the year used to begin with the month of March, so February was then the last month of the year. That is why the extra day in a leap year is added at the end of February.

Since the months are not all the same length some confusion is likely to be experienced when we wish to make plans several weeks ahead. For instance, suppose it is agreed that a cricket match shall take place exactly four weeks after, say, Saturday, May 10th, in a certain year. What date in June will that be? The simplest way to find out, of course, is to consult a calendar. But suppose a calendar is not immediately available, how shall we reckon the date?

Since the month of May contains 31 days, that is, four weeks and three days, the Saturdays in June will occur on dates three days earlier than the Saturdays in May. Therefore, the date of the match should be fixed for June 7.

For similar reasons, the Saturdays in July will occur on dates two days earlier than those in June, since June contains four weeks and two days. Now, as Saturdays in May in the year we are considering occur on May 3rd, 10th, 17th, 24th and 31st, the Saturdays in June will occur on June 7th, 14th, 21st, 28th; and those in July on July 5th, 12th, 19th, 26th.

Rents on farms and other property are usually paid on what are called " Quarter Days ".

In England, Wales and Northern Ireland the Quarter days are

Lady Day	March 25th;	Michaelmas	September 29th;
Midsummer	June 24th;	Christmas	December 25th.

In Scotland they are different, and are called " Term Days ". These occur on

Candlemas	February 2nd;	Lammas	August 1st;
Whitsunday	(this varies from year to year);	Martinmas	November 11th.

EXERCISE XXXIII

1. Which of the following years are leap years:

    1800; 1815; 1837; 1860; 1875; 1896; 1900; 1910; 1912; 1932; 1945; 1948?

2. Write down all the leap years between the year 1896 and the year 1946.

3. On what date does the 75th day of an ordinary year fall?

4. On which day of an ordinary year does each of the following dates occur, and how many more days, in each case, are there to the end of the year:

    January 20th; February 16th; March 17th; June 30th; August 15th; September 23rd?

D.L.M.

5. On which day of a leap year does each of the following dates occur, and how many days, in each case, are there to the end of the year:

   February 18th; March 21st; May 17th; June 21st; September 23rd; December 22nd?

6. How many days are there from February 16th to June 30th in an ordinary year? (Use the results you got in Question 4.)

7. How many days are there, in a leap year, from February 22nd to September 21st?

8. Express, in weeks and extra days, the interval of time in an ordinary year, from January 10th to August 10th.

9. In an ordinary year, there are 52 weeks and 1 day more. New Year's Day in a certain ordinary year fell upon a Thursday; on which day of the week would it fall in the following year?

10. In a certain leap year, New Year's Day fell upon a Sunday. On which day of the week would it fall in the following year?

11. In a leap year, a boy's birthday, February 9th, fell on Tuesday. On which day of the week would it fall in the following year? Another boy's birthday was on March 9th. On which days of the week did it fall in the leap year and in the following year?

12. The dates of Saturdays in June of a certain year were:

   5th; 12th; 19th; 26th.

   Write down the dates of Saturdays in August and September

13. The first Monday in December in a certain year fell on the 4th of the month. Write down the dates of all the Mondays in November of that year.

14. In a certain year June 1st fell on Friday. Write down the dates of all the Fridays in June of the following ordinary year.

15. How many leap years were there from 1911 to 1929 inclusive?

16. How many days are there in the years 1911 to 1929 inclusive?

17. Divide the total number of days in the answer to Question 16 by 235 to the nearest tenth. (The answer to this is the interval of time between one full moon and the next, because there are 235 " moons " in 19 years.)

EXERCISE XXXIV

1. How many days are there in the four quarters:

Lady Day to Midsummer;
Midsummer to Michaelmas;
Michaelmas to Christmas;
Christmas to Lady Day?

2. How many days are there in the present year in each of the Scottish Terms:

Candlemas to Whitsunday;
Whitsunday to Lammas;
Lammas to Martinmas;
Martinmas to Candlemas?

3. A ship set sail on a voyage on December 10th, and reached its destination on March 12th. How many days was it at sea?

4. The rates on a house were due to be paid in full on March 25th. A tenant removed from the house on February 16th (in a year not a leap year). How many days relief of rates could he claim? (You may count either February 16th or March 25th but not both days.)

5. There are four days in the year that are interesting because of the connections with the seasons; the longest, and shortest days, and the equinoxes.

The longest day occurs about June 21st (sometimes on June 22nd).
The shortest day occurs about December 22nd.
The spring equinox occurs about March 21st.
The autumnal equinox occurs about September 23rd.

Calculate the number of days between:

    (*a*) the shortest day and the spring equinox,
    (*b*) the spring equinox and the longest day,
    (*c*) the longest day and the autumnal equinox,
    (*d*) the autumnal equinox and the shortest day.

6. From the following table of sunrise and sunset in London, calculate the length of day, that is, the interval of time between sunrise and sunset, and so show that the longest day occurs about June 21st.

	June 7	June 14	June 21	June 28	July 5
Sunrise (a.m.)	3.47	3.44	3.45	3.47	3.52
Sunset (p.m.)	8.11	8.16	8.18	8.19	8.17

7. From the following table of sunrise and sunset in London, calculate the length of day, and show that the shortest day occurs
about December 22nd.

	Dec. 8	Dec. 15	Dec. 22	Dec. 29	Jan. 5
Sunrise (a.m.)	7.54	8.1	8.6	8.8	8.7
Sunset (p.m.)	3.50	3.49	3.51	3.56	4.4

8. At the equinoxes, the length of day is almost the same as the
length of night, as we can see from the following particulars:

	March 21	September 23
Sunrise (a.m.)	6.3	5.48
Sunset (p.m.)	6.12	5.56

Calculate the lengths of day and night on each of these dates.

(The reason why the day on each of these dates is rather more than
12 hours is this: we continue to see the sun for a few minutes after it
has set because the light from it gets bent slightly in coming through
the earth's atmosphere near the horizon; we see the sun a few minutes
before it actually rises for the same reason.)

9. From the particulars in Questions 6 and 7, calculate the difference between the length of day on the longest day and that on the
shortest day.

10. From the following particulars, calculate the average daily increase, in minutes, of the length of day (*a*) in February, (*b*) in
March:

	Feb. 1st	March 1st	April 1st
Sunrise (a.m.)	7.40	6.47	5.38
Sunset (p.m.)	4.48	5.39	6.31

VII

PERCENTAGES

IN the daily newspapers we often read the words " per cent ". Here are two extracts from a newspaper:

    (i) Only 90 per cent of the candidates who should have taken the examination sat for it, and of those who sat, 71 per cent passed;

    (ii) An advertisement said " This Salad Cream contains 25 per cent of edible oil ".

Let us see what is meant by each of these statements. The first statement, that 90 per cent of those who should have taken the examination actually sat for it, means that 90 candidates out of every 100 who should have done so, did actually sit for the examination.

Now suppose that 2,000 candidates should have sat for the examination.

$$\text{The number who sat} = \frac{90}{100} \text{ of } 2{,}000$$

$$= \frac{9}{10} \text{ of } 2{,}000$$

$$= 1{,}800 \text{ candidates};$$

And, since 71 per cent of those who sat, passed the examination, 71 out of every 100 of those who sat passed it. Therefore,

$$\text{the number who passed} = \frac{71}{100} \text{ of } 1{,}800;$$

(cancelling by 100)

$$= 71 \times 18$$

$$= 1{,}278 \text{ candidates passed.}$$

Now, what is meant by the second newspaper extract?

Simply this, that 25 parts (by weight) out of every 100 parts, that is, $\frac{1}{4}$ of the total weight of Salad Cream sold, is edible oil.

If the weight of the salad cream in a bottle were 6 ounces, then in the cream there should be

$$\tfrac{1}{4} \text{ of } 6 \text{ oz. of edible oil;}$$

that is, $1\tfrac{1}{2}$ oz. of edible oil.

Thus we see that it is a simple matter to calculate a given percentage of anything.

There are some percentages which can be represented as simple fractions; for instance, 50 per cent means 50 out of every hundred; which may be written $\frac{50}{100}$; this is equal to one-half. Therefore 50 per cent of anything is one-half of that thing. Here are a few examples:

50 per cent of £1 is 10s.;
50 per cent of a ton of coal is 10 cwts. of coal;
50 per cent of 80 examination marks is 40 marks.

In a restaurant a waiter asked a customer how he would like his coffee. The customer replied " fifty-fifty ". By this he meant 50 per cent coffee and 50 per cent milk, in other words, half-a-cup of coffee and half-a-cup of milk.

The values of some other percentages, expressed as fractions, should be committed to memory:

25 per cent = one-quarter = $\frac{1}{4}$;
12$\frac{1}{2}$ per cent = one-eighth = $\frac{1}{8}$;
10 per cent = one-tenth = $\frac{1}{10}$.

Here are some examples in which these fractions may be used.

A joint of beef weighed 4 lb. 12 oz. 25 per cent of it was bone. What was the weight of the beef?

Bone = 25 per cent of 4 lb. 12 oz.
= one-quarter of 4 lb. 12 oz.
= 1 lb. 3 oz.

Therefore, the weight of the beef

= 3 lb. 9 oz.

In a school there were 560 pupils. 12$\frac{1}{2}$ per cent of them were under 12 years of age. How many were 12 years old and over?

Number under 12 years old = 12$\frac{1}{2}$ per cent of 560
= one-eighth of 560
= 70.

Therefore, the number of pupils, 12 years old and over

= 560 − 70
= 480.

A property repairer's bill for a job was £7 10s. Ten per cent of it
was for materials, the rest for workmen's wages. How much did the
materials cost, and how much the wages?

$$\begin{aligned}
\text{Materials cost 10 per cent of £7 10s.} \\
= \text{one-tenth of £7 10s.} \\
= 15\text{s.} \\
\text{Wages cost £7 10s.} - 15\text{s.} \\
= £6\ 15\text{s.}
\end{aligned}$$

Frequently the symbol % is used instead of the words " per cent ",
so if we see, say, 60%, we should read it as " 60 per cent ".

If you want to find 60% of anything, first find 10% of it and then
multiply by 6.

To find 70% of anything, first find 10% and then multiply by 7,
and so on.

EXERCISE XXXV

1. Write down the values of the following:

50 per cent of 80 marks.
25 per cent of 60 marks.
75 per cent of 120 marks.
10 per cent of 80 marks.
30 per cent of 80 marks.
70 per cent of 80 marks.

2. Write down the values of the following:

75 per cent of £4.   40 per cent of £5.
10 per cent of £5.   60 per cent of £5.
30 per cent of £5.   90 per cent of £5.

3. Write down the values of the following:

50% of 5 feet.   60% of 2 ft. 6 ins.
25% of 7 feet.   40% of 4 ft. 2 ins.
10% of 9 ft. 2 ins.   90% of 5 ft. 10 ins.

4. Write down the values of the following:

50% of 5 lb. 6 oz. $12\frac{1}{2}$% of 1 cwt.
25% of 6 yds. 2 ft. $37\frac{1}{2}$% of 1 cwt.
$12\frac{1}{2}$% of 5 yds. 1 ft. $62\frac{1}{2}$% of 1 cwt.

5. Write down the values of the following:

$12\frac{1}{2}\%$ of £1 12s.	60% of £1 15s.
10% of £2 10s.	40% of £2 5s.
40% of £3 10s.	30% of £4 5s.

6. Calculate the values of the following:

50% of £1 12s. 6d.	10% of £5 12s. 6d.
25% of 13 ft. 8 ins.	30% of 4 tons 15 cwts.
75% of 8 lb. 6 oz.	60% of 15 yds. 1 ft. 3 ins.

7. 2,370 candidates sat for an examination. 10% of them failed. How many passed?

8. A garden fertilizer consisted of the following ingredients:

Sulphate of Ammonia	50%,
Sulphate of Iron	25%,
Superphosphates	25%.

How many ounces of each of these ingredients are there in 3 pounds of the mixture?

9. When making concrete a workman mixed sand, stones and cement in the following proportions:

Sand 60%,   Stones 20%,   Cement 20%.

How many cubic feet of each of these ingredients should there be in 15 cubic feet of the mixture?

10. The seating accommodation in a cinema is 800. 10% of the seats were 3s. 6d.; 20% were 2s. 9d.; 50% were 1s. 9d.; the rest were 1s. 3d. How many seats were there at each of the prices?

11. The total marks in an examination was 160. The highest mark in the examination was 80% of the total; the lowest 25%. How many marks did the highest and the lowest candidates score?

12. 75% of the total marks in an examination were required for a Pass with Distinction. The total marks were 600. Calculate the Pass with Distinction mark.

13. The maximum mark in a history examination was 120. The highest mark in it was 108; the next to the highest was 96. Express these as percentages.

On page 135 we calculated 90% of a given number by the fraction-method. In that case the calculation was quite simple. Frequently, however, cancelling does not simplify the calculation. Here is an example that will show this.

What is 72% of 312?

$$72\% \text{ of } 312 = \frac{72}{100} \text{ of } 312.$$

If we cancel 72 and 100 by 4 and we get,

$$72\% \text{ of } 312 = \frac{18}{25} \text{ of } 312$$
$$= \frac{18 \times 312}{25}.$$

Here is the rest of the working:

$$
\begin{array}{r}
312 \times 18 \\
\hline
3120 \\
2496 \\
\hline
5616
\end{array}
$$

$$
\begin{array}{r}
224 \cdot 64 \\
\hline
25 \overline{)5616} \\
50 \\
\hline
61 \\
50 \\
\hline
116 \\
100 \\
\hline
160 \\
150 \\
\hline
100 \\
100 \\
\hline
\cdots
\end{array}
$$

Thus we see that cancelling makes the working rather long because it leaves us with a division by 25.

Let us do the same calculation, without cancelling.

$$72\% \text{ of } 312 = \frac{72 \times 312}{100}.$$

Here is the working.

$$312 \times 72$$
$$\overline{21840}$$
$$624$$
$$\overline{22464}$$

Dividing this by 100, we get

$$224 \cdot 64,$$

the same answer as by the other method.

This then is the general method:

" To find a certain percentage of a given quantity or number, multiply the quantity or number by the percentage and divide by 100." Let us use it in the following examples:

What is 17% of 125?

$$17\% \text{ of } 125 = \frac{125 \times 17}{100}.$$

$$125 \times 17$$
$$\overline{1250}$$
$$875$$
$$\overline{2125}$$

Therefore, 17% of $125 = 21 \cdot 25.$

What is 23% of 62 cubic feet?

$$23\% \text{ of } 62 \text{ cubic feet} = \frac{62 \times 23}{100} \text{ cu. ft.}$$

$$62 \times 23$$
$$\overline{1240}$$
$$186$$
$$\overline{1426}$$

Therefore, 23% of 62 cubic feet $= 14 \cdot 26$ cubic feet.

This method is especially valuable in finding percentages of £ s. d., as we shall see in Book Two.

Thus we have seen that percentages are fractions, more simply expressed, and therefore more suitable for use by the general public.

Percentages are simpler than ordinary and decimal fractions, because they are usually expressed in whole numbers.

Let us consider the following rectangle, which may represent a plot of land.

It is divided into 6 unequal parts, I, II, III, IV, V, VI.

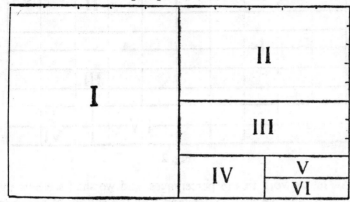

Fig. 1

Part I $=\frac{1}{2}$ of the whole plot;

Part II $=\frac{1}{4}$ of the whole plot;

Part III $=\frac{3}{5}$ of the size of Part II;

$=\frac{3}{5}$ of $\frac{1}{4}$ of the whole plot

$=\frac{3}{20}$ of the whole plot;

Part IV $=\frac{1}{2}$ of $\frac{2}{5}$ of $\frac{1}{4}$ of the whole plot

$=\frac{1}{20}$ of the whole plot;

Parts V and VI are equal,

each $=\frac{1}{2}$ of Part IV

$=\frac{1}{40}$ of the whole plot.

Thus, Parts I, II, III, IV, V and VI are, respectively:

$\frac{1}{2}$, $\frac{1}{4}$, $\frac{3}{20}$, $\frac{1}{20}$, $\frac{1}{40}$ and $\frac{1}{40}$ of the whole plot.

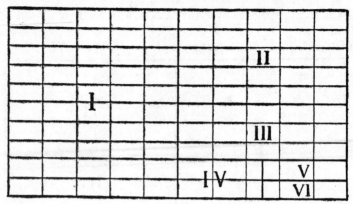

Fig. 2

Now let us work this in percentages, and we shall see how much easier it is, and we shall understand why the editors of newspapers prefer to use percentages in their papers.

Fig. 2 shows the plot divided into 100 parts. From it we see at a glance that

Part I   contains 50 small parts, that is, 50 per cent of the whole;
Part II   ,,   25   ,,   ,,   ,, ,, 25 ,, ,,   ,, ,, ,,
Part III   ,,   15   ,,   ,,   ,, ,, 15 ,, ,,   ,, ,, ,,
Part IV   ,,   5   ,,   ,,   ,, ,,   5 ,, ,,   ,, ,, ,,
Part V   ,, $2\frac{1}{2}$,,   ,,   ,, ,, $2\frac{1}{2}$,, ,,   ,, ,, ,,
Part VI   ,, $2\frac{1}{2}$,,   ,,   ,, ,, $2\frac{1}{2}$,, ,,   ,, ,, ,,

Examination marks are usually expressed as percentages.

If the total possible marks in an examination were 100, then the actual marks obtained by an individual denotes the percentage of marks obtained.

For instance, a teacher set 10 questions in a history examination, and offered 10 marks for each, all the ten questions to be attempted.

A boy got the following marks on successive questions:

$$3, 9, 6, 6, 4, 10, 2, 7, 5, 0.$$

What percentage of marks did he get?

His total = 52.

His percentage = 52.

If the total possible marks is not 100, then it is necessary to do a short calculation to turn the marks obtained into percentages.

Example 1. Suppose a candidate got 36 marks out of 80 in an examination. What percentage is that?

Evidently he got $\frac{36}{80}$ of the total marks. Had the total been 100, he would have got the same fraction of 100 marks.

$$\frac{36}{80} \text{ of } 100 = \frac{36}{80} \times 100,$$

(cancelling by 20)
$$= \frac{36}{80} \times 100$$

$$= \frac{36 \times 5}{4}$$

(cancelling by 4)
$$= \frac{36 \times 5}{4}$$

$$= 45$$

Thus, 36 out of 80 = 45 per cent.

We might have done this without cancelling, as follows:

$$\frac{36}{80} \text{ of } 100 = \frac{36 \times 100}{80}$$

$$= \frac{3600}{80}$$

$$\begin{array}{r} 45 \\ 80 \overline{\smash{)}3600} \end{array}$$

Therefore, 36 out of 80 = 45%.

Example 2. In an examination a candidate obtained 90 marks out of a total of 150. What percentage is that?

$$90 \text{ out of } 150 = \frac{90}{150} \times 100\%$$

$$= \frac{9000}{150}\%$$

$$\begin{array}{r} 60 \\ 150 \overline{\smash{)}9000} \end{array}$$

Therefore, 90 marks out of 150 = 60%.

A Percentage Ready-Reckoner can be quickly made from a piece of graph paper such as was used for the weight chart on page 108, Question 3, Exercise XXIX.

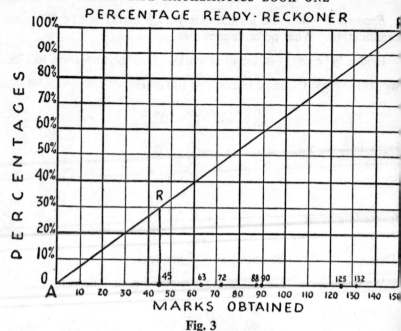

Fig. 3

Example 3. Make a Percentage Ready-Reckoner in which the highest mark is 150.

Along the axis which runs from left to right, let 1 division represent 2 marks; make a scale of marks from 0 to 150.

Along the axis at right-angles to this axis, make a percentage scale in which 1 division represents 2%.

Put a cross at the point P which corresponds to 150 marks on the marks-scale and to 100% on the percentage-scale.

Join P to the point A, the zero mark on both axes, by a straight line. This, then is the Percentage Ready-Reckoner.

Example 4. By means of the Percentage Ready-Reckoner just made, (Fig. 3) express as percentages, the following marks out of 150:

45, 63, 72, 88, 90, 125, 132.

Along the MARKS OBTAINED axis put a cross at 45, and read off the percentage corresponding to the point R above it. This, you will see, is 29% approximately.

Do likewise for the rest of the marks and you will get the following percentages:

29%, 42%, 48%, 58%, 60%, 83%, 88%.

EXERCISE XXXVI

1. In an examination eight questions were set, on each of which the maximum mark was 15. These were a candidate's marks:

$$5, 0, 8, 6, 6, 2, 8, 5.$$

What percentage of marks did that candidate obtain?

2. Here is a table of marks obtained by four boys. The numbers in brackets are the maximum marks in each subject.

Name	English (100)	Maths. (150)	Hist. (60)	Geog. (60)	Handicrafts (120)	Totals ( )
Andrews	62	72	45	54	90	
Bertram	56	63	42	39	102	
Cobley	75	105	54	54	90	
Dawson	60	84	51	45	72	

(*a*) find the total marks obtained by each.

Arrange the boys in order of merit; and

(*b*) calculate the percentages of the marks gained by each boy in each subject;

(*c*) calculate the percentage of the total marks in the examinations gained by each boy.

3. During a whole year a boy made 355 attendance out of a possible 375. What fraction of the possible attendances did he make? Express this as a percentage of the total attendances.

4. The total number of voters entitled to vote in an election was 4,560. Only 2,750 voted. What fraction of the electors voted? Express this fraction as a percentage.

5. Make a Percentage Ready-Reckoner in which 140 marks correspond to 100% and from it read the percentages corresponding to the following marks:

$$25, 38, 42, 55, 64, 70, 95, 115, 120, 125.$$

6. Make a Percentage Ready-Reckoner in which the maximum mark of 85 shall correspond to 100%, and from it read the percentages corresponding to the following marks:

$$38, 45, 50, 62, 68, 70 \ 75, 77, 82.$$

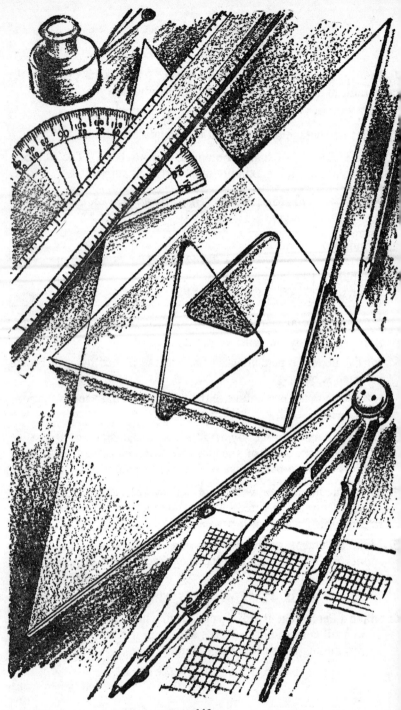

VIII

ANGULAR MEASUREMENT

Set-squares

In Chapter II, when we were making dimensioned drawings, we used set-squares for setting out *right angles*. You probably noticed that set-squares are not all the same shape, but with any of them it is possible to set out a right angle because every set-square has one of its angles a right angle. Set-squares are usually sold in pairs; one of a pair is shaped like the one in Fig. 1 below, the other like the one in Fig. 2.

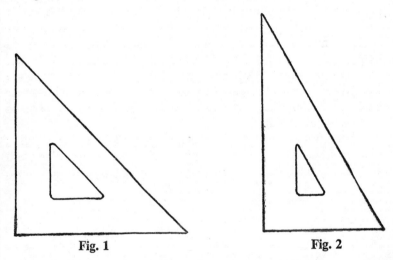

Fig. 1   Fig. 2

You should examine a pair of set-squares very carefully; you will find that, in those like Fig. 1, the two edges which form the right angle are exactly the same length. In those like Fig. 2 no two edges are alike, but the shortest edge is exactly one-half the length of the longest edge.

When you get a new pair of set-squares it is advisable, before you use them, to test them. The first test should be to see if the angles are right angles. How shall we do this? Stand them upright, one

L   147   D.L.M.

behind the other, on a smooth surface—a drawing-board or a table top—as shown in Fig. 3.

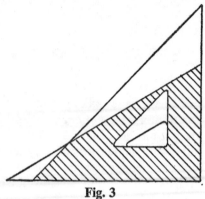

Fig. 3

If the upright edge of one is exactly behind that of the other, this is an indication that they *may* be *true*, but this test, so far, is not conclusive; it merely shows that the angles that are being tested are equal. They may be less than right angles, greater than right angles, or exactly right angles. A further test is necessary: this we shall see presently. If the two upright edges do not fit—you can tell whether or not they do by feeling along the edge—one or the other, or perhaps both of them cannot be true.

The next test is to place them edge to edge as shown in Fig. 4, the lower edges resting on the drawing-board as before. You will notice in the sketch that the two upright edges do not fit close to each

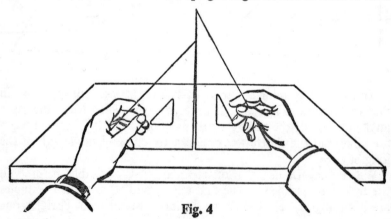

Fig. 4

other; there is a gap at the bottom; this tells us that the angles, if equal, are greater than right angles. Only if the two upright edges fit together from bottom to top, provided the angles are equal, can we say the angles are true right angles.

How shall we make a pair of set-squares if we have not already got one to copy from, or another means of measuring the right angles?

First we must find a practical method of making a right angle: a method such as a joiner or cabinet-maker would use in a workshop.

Take a strip of paper about four of five inches wide. With a straight-edge and a sharp pocket knife, cut one of the long edges of the paper perfectly straight. This edge is marked *AB* in Fig. 5, and make *DC* parallel to *AB*.

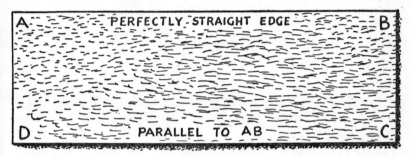

Fig. 5

Now, fold the right-hand half over the left-hand half so that the straight edge from *B* fits exactly over that from *A*. Then press the crease *EF* firmly down (Fig. 6). This crease is exactly at right angles to the edge *AB*. That is, the angle *BEF* is a *true* right angle.

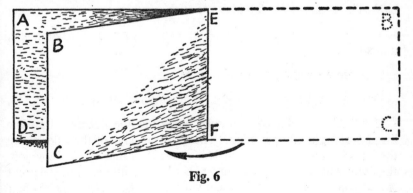

Fig. 6

With straight-edge and pocket-knife cut along the crease and remove the right-hand portion, then the remaining piece has two parallel edges, *AE* and *DF*, and the angle *AEF* is exactly a right angle.

Now, fold the paper so that the edge *EF* fits exactly over the edge *AE*, the point *F* being directly over point *H*, making the crease *EG*.

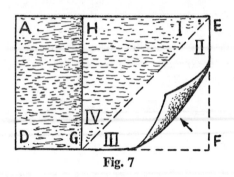

Fig. 7

If you join *G* to *H* you will have the figure *EFGH* which is a square, divided by the *diagonal EG*, into two right-angled triangles *EGF* and *EGH* (Fig. 7).

Either of these two triangles might be used as a *template* or pattern, from which to make a set-square like that in Fig. 1, page 147.

You will notice that the angle I=the angle II. Since these two angles together make a complete right angle, each of these angles is half of a right angle.

Similarly, each of the angles III and IV is half of a right angle.

With this kind of set-square we can draw directly, right angles and half right angles. We can also use such a set-square in order to get some other angles; for instance, $\frac{1}{4}$ of a right angle, $\frac{3}{4}$ of a right angle, and so on.

Suppose we want $\frac{1}{4}$ of a right angle.

Draw $\frac{1}{2}$ a right angle *CAB* by means of your set-square. (Fig. 8).

Lay the lower edge of your ruler along the line *AB*, and draw the line *LL* along the upper edge. Then lay one edge of the ruler along the line *AC*, and draw the line *MM* along the other edge. Now join the point where the lines *LL* and *MM* cross, or intersect, to the point *A* and you will see that this line divides the angle *CAB*, which is half

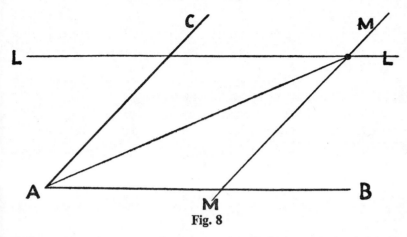

Fig. 8

a right angle, into two equal parts, so each of them will be a quarter of a right angle.

Now let us draw an angle equal to $\frac{3}{4}$ of a right angle.

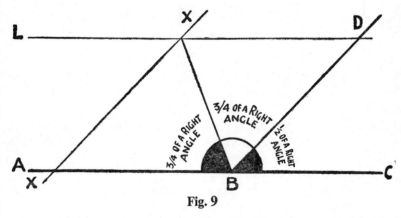

Fig. 9

Draw a line *ABC*, and at the point *B* set out with your set-square the angle *CBD* equal to half a right angle. The angle *ABD* will be $1\frac{1}{2}$ right angles; now find one-half of this angle in the way you found one-half of the angle *CAB* in the last example (Fig. 8), using your ruler to draw the lines *LD* and *XX*, parallel respectively to *AB* and *BD*.

Join the point of intersection of *LD* and *XX* to *B* and you will see that the angle *ABD* is divided by it into 2 equal parts, each of which equals $\frac{3}{4}$ of a right angle.

Fig. 10 below represents two roads, London Road and Market Street, crossing each other *at right angles*; that is, the centre lines of the roads, shown dotted in the diagram, cross each other *at right angles*.

It will be seen that at the point of intersection of the centre lines of the roads, there are *four right angles*. This is what we mean when we say, " round a point there are four right angles ".

We shall need this fact when we set out to make a template with which to make a set-square like the one marked in Fig. 2 on page 147.

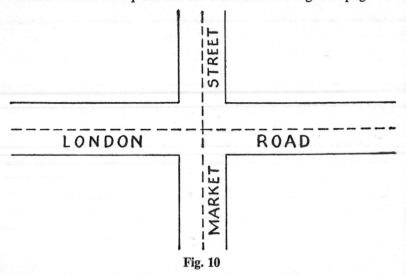

Fig. 10

In the set-square, Fig. 2, page 147, one of the angles is a right angle. What part of a right angle is each of the other two angles?

We shall be able to find out if we make a template from which to mark out the set-square.

Draw a line *AB* equal in length to the length of the longest side of the set-square you wish to make (Fig 11).

Put the point of the compasses at the point *A* and open them out so as to draw a circle passing through the point *B*. Now, put the point of the compasses at the point *B*, and mark off the point *C*, on the circumference of the circle, so that *BC* is the same length as *AB*. Then join the points *C* and *A*, and you will find the triangle *ACB* has all of its sides the same length.

If you now cut out this triangle and fold it (see Fig. 12) so that the point *B* fits over the point *A*, you will have a template for making the set-square like Fig. *B*. The angle at *P* will be the right angle.

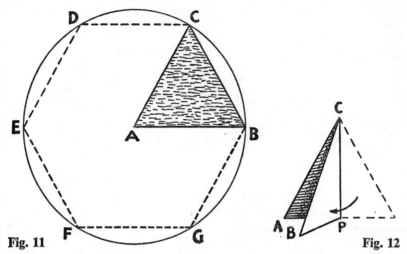

Fig. 11   Fig. 12

You can now see why the shortest side of this set-square is one-half of the longest side.

Triangles which are the same shape as the triangle *ABC* are called by a special name: *equilateral*, which means *equal-sided*. No matter which way we turn a triangle of the same size and shape as triangle *ABC* it will fit exactly over the triangle *ABC*; this is because the angles at *A*, *B* and *C* are all the same size.

Can you see that the small angle of the template is half as big as the angle at *A*?

Let us now see what fraction of a right angle the angle at *A* is.

On the circumference of the circle you will find points *D*, *E*, *F* and *G*. These points were all found by stepping off distances with the compasses as we did when we found the position of the point *C*. If we were to join each of these points to *A* we should have six equilateral triangles, all the same size as the triangle *ABC*. Now round the point *A* we could fit 4 right angles; therefore, each of the angles at *A* would be $\frac{1}{6}$ of 4 right angles; that is, each of the angles at *A* would be $\frac{4}{6}$ of a right angle; that is, $\frac{2}{3}$ of a right angle.

So, in the set-square, we have one right angle; an angle equal to $\frac{2}{3}$ of a right angle; and since the smallest angle is one-half of the angle at *C*, it is $\frac{1}{3}$ of a right angle.

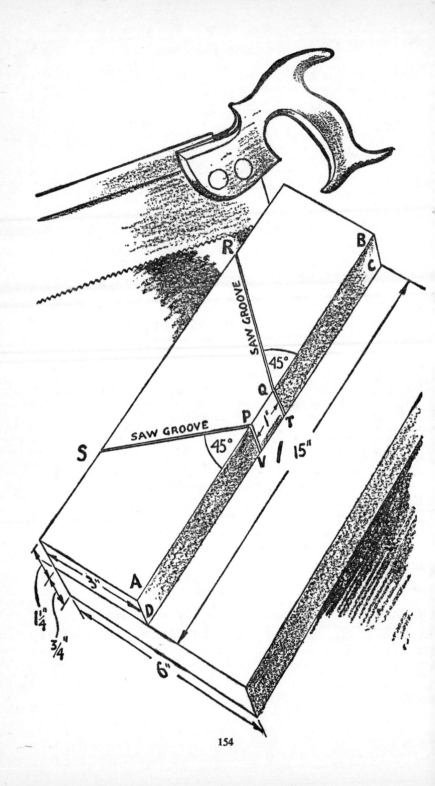

SAW GROOVE

45°

SAW GROOVE

45°

R

B

C

Q

P

T

1"

S

V

15"

A

D

3"

1¼"

¾"

6"

154

A *try-square* (Fig. 13) is used in workshops for setting-out right angles on wood, and for testing right angles when you are planing the edges of a piece of wood *true*.

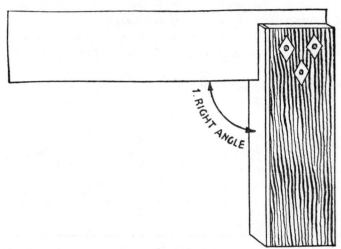

Fig. 13

If you examine the corner of a picture frame, or of the moulding round a panel of a door, you will see that the pieces of moulding are cut obliquely, each at $\frac{1}{2}$ a right angle, to form the joint. Such a joint is called a *mitre-joint*. Here are instructions for making a *mitre-block* which can be used for cutting mitre-joints.

Plane two pieces of hardwood to the given dimensions and glue and screw them together as shown in the sketch opposite.

Set a slide-bevel, Fig. 19, to 45 degrees with a 45° set-square, and mark the lines *SP* and *QR* at 45° to *AB*.

Draw *PV* and *QT* at right angles to *CD*.

With a fine tenon saw, make saw grooves along *SP*, *PV*, and *RQ*, *QT*, through the upper block.

The mitre-block is then ready for use.

Method of using a mitre-block.

To mitre the left-hand end of a piece of moulding, lay the moulding flat on the base, and press it tightly against the block containing the saw grooves, with the end to be mitred a little to the left of the upright part *VP* of the saw groove. Place the tenon saw in the groove *SPV* and saw through the moulding. Then the left-hand end of the moulding will be mitred as required.

The protractor

The right angle is too large a unit for general use. A smaller unit, called a degree, is much more convenient. A degree is got by dividing the four right angles round a point into 360 parts; each of the parts is called 1 degree, and this is usually written 1°.

A protractor is an instrument which is graduated in degrees. The simplest form of protractor is a semicircle as shown in Fig. 14.

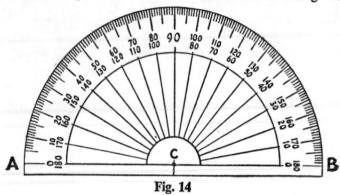

Fig. 14

With a protractor like this it is possible to measure—or draw—angles up to 2 right angles, that is 180°.

The angles of the set-square, Fig. 1, page 147, are 1 right angle, and $\frac{1}{2}$ a right angle; that is, 90° and 45°, so we call that set-square a " 45° set-square ".

The angles of the set-square, Fig. 2, page 147, are 1 right angle, $\frac{2}{3}$ of a right angle and $\frac{1}{3}$ of a right angle; that is, 90°, 60°, 30°, so we call it a " 60° set-square ", or a " 30° set-square ".

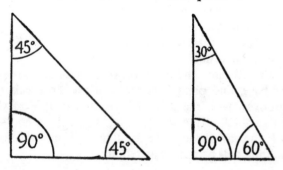

Fig. 15

Fig. 16

EXERCISE XXXVII

1. Draw, and cut out of paper, a square *ABCD*, sides 2 inches long. The diagonals *AC* and *BD* cross at the point *E*.

Fold along *BD*. The point *C* fits exactly over the point *A*. What can you conclude about the angles *EAB* and *ECB*, and about the angle at which *AC* and *BD* cross each other?

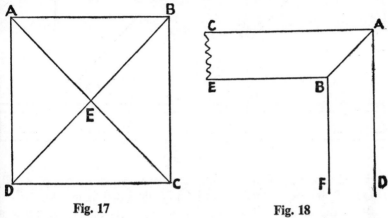

Fig. 17   Fig. 18

2. Fig. 18 is a drawing of two pieces of moulding round a door-frame. They are *mitred* along the joint *BA*. What angle does the joint *BA* make with the edges *AC* and *AD*; and with the edges *EB* and *BF*?

3. A carpenter uses a *slide-bevel* for marking oblique cuts across parallel pieces of wood. He can alter the angle by loosening the fixing screw. If the angle between the stock and the blade on the left-hand side of the stock be half a right angle, what is the angle between the stock and blade on the right of the stock?

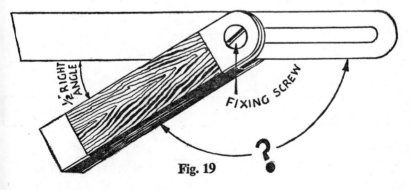

Fig. 19

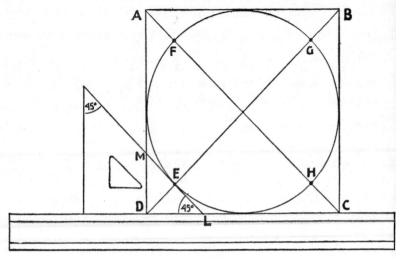

Fig. 20

4. Fig. 20 shows how a carpenter converts a square piece of wood, *ABCD*, into an *octagon*, that is, an eight-sided figure.

With the intersection of the diagonals, *K*, as centre, he draws a circle touching the sides of the square, cutting the diagonals in the points *E, F, G, H*. Then, by placing the ruler along the edge *DC*, and sliding the 45 degree set-square along it until the sloping edge touches the circle at *E*, he draws the line *LM*. This is one of the sides of the octagon. Complete the figure in a square, sides $2\frac{1}{2}$ inches long. How many degrees are there in the angle *MLC*?

5. With compasses and a 60 degrees set-square, draw a *hexagonal* nut in a circle 1 inch radius.

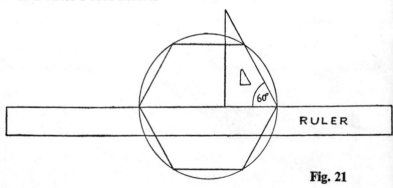

Fig. 21

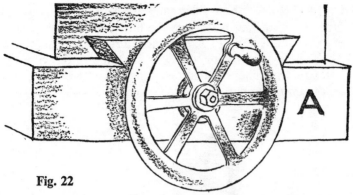

Fig. 22

6. How many degrees are there in the angle between consecutive spokes in the wheel marked A (Fig. 22)?

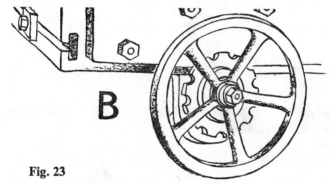

Fig. 23

7. How many degrees are there in the angle between consecutive spokes in the wheel marked B (Fig. 23).

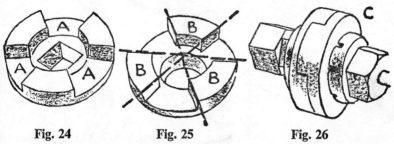

Fig. 24   Fig. 25   Fig. 26

8. The two machined parts shown in Fig. 24 and 25 fit together to form the coupling shown in Fig. 26. Calculate the number of degrees in the angles between the dotted lines shown in Fig. 25.

Drawing parallel lines with a ruler and set-square

In order to draw lines parallel to the line marked *PPP*, place one edge of a set-square along *PPP*, then place a ruler along another edge as shown below. By sliding the set-square along the edge of the ruler you can draw lines parallel to *PPP*. In the position shown in Fig. 27, the third line parallel to *PPP* is being drawn.

Fig. 27

If the ruler has been held firmly on the paper, and the set-square close to the ruler, then the lines will be parallel. The angles marked *A, B, C, D* should be equal. This fact gives us a test of parallelism.

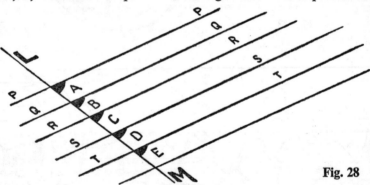

Fig. 28

Suppose we wish to test whether the lines *PP, QQ, RR, SS, TT* are parallel. Let us draw any line *LM* across them. With a protractor, we measure the number of degrees in each of the angles *A, B, C, D, E*. If these angles are equal, then the lines are parallel. In Fig. 28 each of the angles *A, B, C, D, E* is 60°; therefore, the lines are parallel.

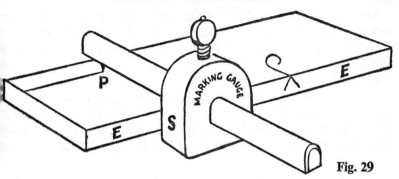

Fig. 29

A carpenter uses a *marking-gauge* for drawing parallel lines on wood. Suppose he wishes to plane a piece of wood 3 inches wide, as for the mitre-block on page 154. First, he planes one edge, say the edge marked E in Fig. 29. He then sets his gauge, so that the distance of the marker, which is a sharp-pointed pin, P, from the stock, S, of the gauge is 3 inches. Then he slides the stock along the edge marked EE; the marker P draws a line on the wood parallel to the edge EE. This is the mark indicating the width to which the wood is to be planed.

Alternate angles

Take a piece of wood that has been planed parallel to a width of about 4 inches. Saw it into two parts along an oblique line as in Fig. 30. The angles marked A and B are called alternate angles. You will find if you place the piece on the left-hand side of the saw-cut on the top of the other piece as shown in Fig. 31, the angle B fits exactly the alternate angle A. This is an important property of parallel lines.

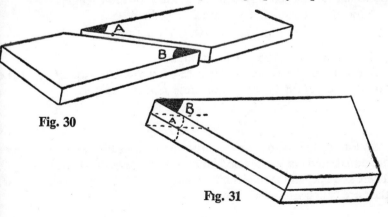

Fig. 30

Fig. 31

We can use this alternate angle property of parallel lines in order to find an important fact about the angles of any triangle.

How many degrees are there in the sum of the three angles of any triangle?

Let *ABC* be any triangle.

Cut it out of thick paper or thin cardboard, and place one of its sides, say *AB*, on the edge of a piece of wood as shown in Fig. 32. Then, by means of a marking gauge, draw a line *MM* on the wood, parallel to the edge, that is to the side *AB* of the triangle, passing through the other angular point *C* of the triangle.

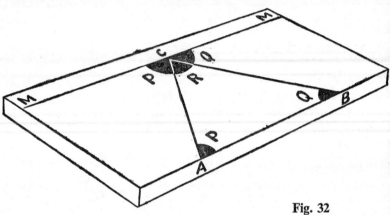

Fig. 32

The alternate angles marked *P* are equal to one another and those marked *Q* are equal to one another; therefore, the three angles of the triangle, *P*, *Q* and *R*, are together equal to the three angles *P*, *R*, *Q*, which form a semicircle at the point *C* of the triangle.

Now, in a semicircle there are 180°; therefore,

the angles $P + Q + R = 180°$.

This is evidently true for all triangles.

We can confirm this is the case of the 45° set-square, and the 60° set-square, for the angles of these set-squares were:

$$90° + 45° + 45° = 180°;$$
$$90° + 60° + 30° = 180°.$$

In the case of the 45° set-square, we saw that the two shorter sides are equal, and the angles opposite to them are equal, each being 45°. There is a special name given to triangles which have two sides equal; they are called *isosceles* triangles.

The angles opposite the equal sides in an isosceles triangles are equal; we can see that this is so by drawing such a triangle and cutting it out in paper; see Fig. 33. Now fold the paper so that the side *AB*, which is equal to the side *AC*, lies along *AC*; you will see that the angles at *B* and *C* are equal because one fits exactly over the other.

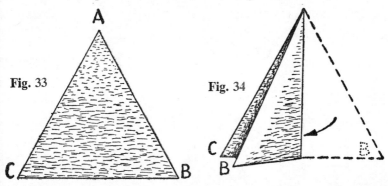

Fig. 33

Fig. 34

If we know the number of degrees in any one of the angles in an isosceles triangle, we can easily calculate the number of degrees in the other two angles. For instance, suppose the angle at *C* contains 65°; then the angle at *B* contains 65°, so the angle at *A* will be got by subtracting twice 65° from 180°;

$$2 \times 65° = 130°; \text{ therefore, the angle at } A = 50°.$$

Again, if the angle at *A* were 40°, each of the angles *B* and *C* would be one-half of (180° − 40°) = one-half of 140° = 70°.

EXERCISE XXXVIII

1. Fig. 35 is a sketch of a template which a wheelwright would use when cutting six pieces of wood for the rim of a wheel. If the lines *PQ* and *RS* were produced until they cross, what would be the angle between them? Calculate the number of degrees in the angle *A* at which the slide-bevel must be set.

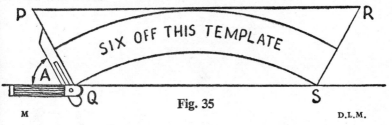

SIX OFF THIS TEMPLATE

Fig. 35

M

2. Calculate the angles marked *S* in the diagram of the segmental arch (Fig. 36), at which the bricks have to be cut for the first of the bricks of the ⟨...⟩ arch to rest upon.

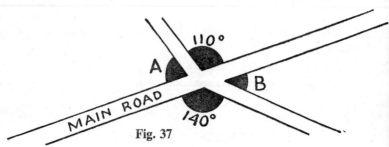

Fig. 36

3. Fig. 37 is a plan of a four-road junction. The main road is straight. Calculate the angles *A* and *B* shown in the plan.

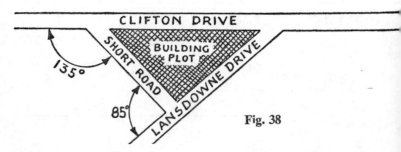

Fig. 37

4. Fig. 38 below shows a plot of building land enclosed by Clifton Drive, Lansdowne Drive and Short Road. From the angles shown, calculate the angles at the three corners of the plot.

CLIFTON DRIVE

BUILDING PLOT

135°

85°

Fig. 38

5. A path was laid across the building-plot in Question **4,** at right angles to Clifton Drive; at what angle would it join Lansdowne Drive?

6. Fig. 39 is the plan of a window seat round the inside of a bay-window.

Calculate the number of degrees in the angles marked *A, B, C.*

If the mitre joint lines were produced until they cross, how many degrees would there be in the angle between them?

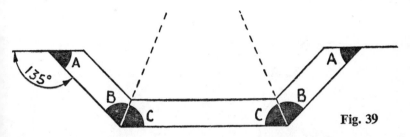

Fig. 39

7. The lines joining *P,* a point inside a 45° set-square, to the corners *A, B, C* of the set-square, bisect the angles at *A, B, C.* Calculate the angles of the three triangles *PAB, PBC* and *PCA.*

8. The lines joining *Q,* a point inside a 60° set-square, to the corners *E, D, F* of the set-square, bisect the angles at *E, D, F.* Calculate the angles of the triangles *QED, QDF,* and *QFE.*

9. *ABCD* is a rectangular board, across which a shallow groove *EF* is cut. The angle *FEB* is 60 degrees.

The lines *EP* and *FP* bisect the angles *FEB* and *EFC* respectively. Calculate the angles of the triangle *EFP.*

The rotation of stars round the Pole Star

There is one point in the sky round which all stars appear to turn or rotate. This star is called the Pole Star. Where is this star? It is not easy to pick out a particular star from the thousands of stars that one can see on a starry night, but it is fairly easy to find a group of stars, or—as a group is generally called—a constellation.

The constellation which most people know is called by various names. Some people call it the Great Bear; others, the Plough; others, Charlie's waggon; in America it is called the Big Dipper. We shall call it the Great Bear.

Now, the Great Bear consists of a very large number of stars, seven of which are brighter than the rest. It is this group of seven stars that is generally called the Great Bear.

Fig. 40 shows the positions of these seven stars with respect to one another.

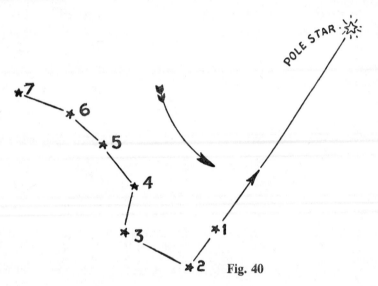

Fig. 40

For purposes of reference we shall number the stars 1, 2, 3, 4, 5, 6, 7.

The stars 1 and 2 are called the Pointers, because the line joining them points to the Pole Star as shown in the diagram.

On a bright night look for the Great Bear and try to find the Pole Star. It will help you to find it if you remember that the distance from star number 1 to the Pole Star is about four times the distance between stars 1 and 2.

In Fig. 40 you will see a curved arrow; this denotes the direction in which all stars turn or rotate round the Pole Star.

How quickly do stars rotate round the Pole Star?

They make a complete revolution round the Pole Star in a day. From this we can calculate the rate per hour, that is, the number of degrees per hour, at which the stars rotate round it.

In a day, the stars turn through an angle of 360°; in an hour they turn through $\frac{360}{24}$ degrees.

$$\begin{array}{r} 15 \text{ degrees per hour} \\ 24\overline{\smash{)}360} \\ \underline{24} \\ 120 \\ \underline{120} \\ \cdots \end{array}$$

Therefore, stars rotate round the Pole Star at the rate of 15 degrees per hour. This is a useful fact to remember, because it will help us to make little predictions as to where a group of stars will be found some time later than when we first observed it.

At 6.0 p.m.—or if we are using a twenty-four hour clock, at 18.00 o'clock—in the early part of October, the Great Bear is in the position shown in Fig. 41.

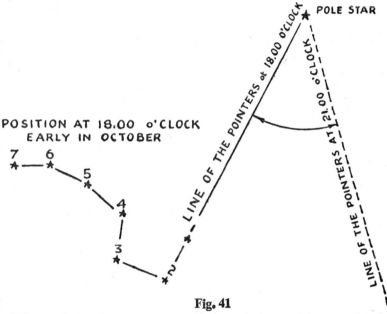

Fig. 41

What will be the position of the Great Bear at 9.0 p.m., that is, 21.00 o'clock, in the early part of October?

The time interval from 6.0 p.m. to 9.0 p.m. is 3 hours.
Angular movement of the Great Bear in 3 hours $= 15° \times 3$
$$= 45°.$$

Therefore the line joining the Pointers will move through 45 degrees.

With a protractor or a 45° set-square, set out an angle of 45 degrees to the line of the Pointers in a counter-clockwise direction as shown in the diagram.

Place a piece of tracing paper over the diagram; put a pin through the tracing paper and the diagram at the position of the Pole Star, and mark on the tracing paper the positions of the remaining stars in the Great Bear.

Now rotate the tracing paper round the pin until the line of the pointers lies on the dotted line. This now gives the positions of the stars in the Great Bear at 9.0 p.m. Prick the positions through the tracing paper to complete the diagram.

EXERCISE XXXIX

1. The Great Bear is in the position shown below (Fig. 42) at 6 p.m. in the early part of January every year.

By means of calculation and drawing on tracing-paper, plot the position of the constellation at 11 p.m.

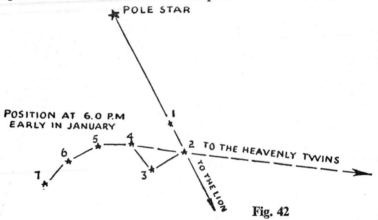

Fig. 42

2. From Fig. 42 plot the position of the Great Bear at two hours after midnight in the early part of January.

3. The line drawn from star 4 to star 2, when produced, points to the position of the Heavenly Twins, Castor and Pollux, which are close together.

Draw a line on the tracing which you made in connection with Question 1; this will show the direction in which to look for these stars at 11 p.m. in the early part of January.

4. The line joining star 1 of the Great Bear to star 2, when produced in the direction opposite to the Pole Star, points to the constellation called The Lion.

Draw a line on the tracing paper which you used in connection with Questions 1 and 2, to show the direction in which to look for The Lion at midnight in the early part of January.

5. The earth describes a path, almost circular, round the sun in a year, that is, in 365 days, approximately.

Calculate, to the nearest degree, its speed in degrees per day, and in degrees per month, reckoning twelve months in a year.

6. Draw a circle, 92 millimetres radius, to represent the path of the earth round the sun.

Choose any point on its circumference to represent the position of the earth on 1st January.

Assuming that the earth moves along the circumference of this circle in a counter-clockwise direction at approximately 1° per day, using your protractor mark the positions of the earth on the circumference on the following dates:

9th February;   21st March;   4th May.

IX

THE THEOREM OF PYTHAGORAS
AND SQUARE ROOTS

The theorem of Pythagoras

In the marking-out of plots of land, foundations of buildings, sports grounds and so forth, the need arises for the setting-out of right angles on a large scale. Set-squares and protractors, of course, are not suitable for this purpose in such conditions.

When the Egyptians were making their large buildings: temples and pyramids, they employed professional right-angle makers, called *rope-stretchers*, to set-out the right angles at the corners. These men were something like our modern surveyors. They were called rope-stretchers because the secret method which they used for setting-out right angles depended upon the stretching of a rope knotted in a special way. We shall see what their secret was, as we use their method in the setting-out of, say, a football-pitch. Instead of a rope, however, we shall use a Surveyor's Chain.

Measuring with a surveyor's chain

Here is an illustration of a Surveyor's Chain.

Fig. 1

The chain is 22 yards long; it is not divided into yards, feet and inches, but into 100 *links*.

At each of the two ends of the chain there is a handle or grip, and at the end of every ten links there is a brass tag attached to the

Fig. 2

chain; these tags are shaped as shown above. By means of the tags one can readily read the measurements, less than a chain, in links.

Lengths measured by means of a chain may be expressed either in links and chains or in chains and decimals of a chain. For example, if a field is 3 chains and 41 links long, this might be recorded as follows:

$$\text{Length of field} = 3 \text{ ch. } 41 \text{ lk.}$$
$$= 3\cdot41 \text{ ch.} \quad \text{(because 1 lk.} = 0\cdot01 \text{ ch.).}$$

Lengths expressed decimally in chains may be converted into yards very readily:

$3\cdot41$ ch. $= 3\cdot41 \times 22$ yds.   (since there are 22 yards in 1 chain)

$$= 75\cdot02 \text{ yds.}$$

$$\begin{array}{r} 3\cdot41 \times 22 \\ \hline 68\cdot2 \\ 6\cdot82 \\ \hline 75\cdot02 \end{array}$$

$$= 75 \text{ yds. approx.}$$

When lengths expressed in yards are to be measured with a chain the yards must be converted into chains to two places of decimals. For instance, convert 150 yards into chains.

$$150 \text{ yds.} = \frac{150}{22} \text{ ch.}$$

$$\begin{array}{r} 6\cdot82 \text{ nearly} \\ 22 \overline{\smash{)}150} \\ 132 \\ \hline 180 \\ 176 \\ \hline 40 \end{array}$$

$$= 6\cdot82 \text{ ch.}$$

$$= 6 \text{ ch. } 82 \text{ lk.}$$

When long distances are to be measured in a given direction, care should be taken so that successive positions of the chain on the ground will be in the same direction.   To ensure this it is customary to erect a *line of poles*.

Fig. 3

In Fig. 3 a line of poles is to be laid down between the two boys on the extreme left and right.

This is how it is done:

(i) the pole *A* is erected at the point on the ground where the line of poles is to begin and pole *C* at a distant point along it.

(ii) the boy holding pole *B*, taking his instructions from the boy on the left of pole *A*, moves his pole until it is in line with poles *A* and *C*.

Then *A*, *B*, *C* is the line of poles.

When the distance between *A* and *C* is great, say up to 100 yards several poles should be erected in line with them.

Setting-out a football pitch

Let us now set-out a Rugby Football Pitch, 110 yards by 75 yards, on the playing field.

1. Drive a stake A in the ground at the point chosen for the middle of the goal posts at one end of the pitch, and set up a line of posts to mark the direction along which the length of the pitch is to be measured.

2. Measure 5 chains, that is 110 yards, from A to B, along this line of posts, and drive in a stake at B (Fig. 4). B will then be the middle of the goal posts at the other end of the pitch.

A   — 5 CHAINS = 110 YARDS —   B

Fig. 4

3. Now set-out the goal-line passing through A (Fig. 4), as follows: along the line of posts AB measure AC (Fig. 5) equal to 30 links, and drive in a stake at C.

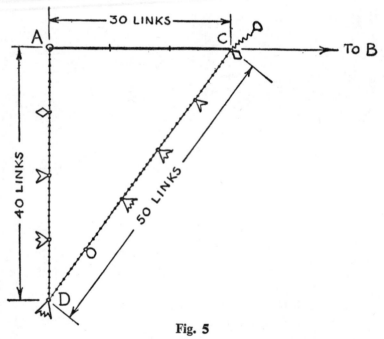

Fig. 5

Let one boy hold one of the grips of the chain at the point *A*, and let another boy, standing at *C*, take hold of the chain at a point (40 + 50) links from *A*'s grip. Thus, between *A* and *C* there is a loop of the chain, 90 links long.

Now, let a third boy, *D*, take hold of the chain at the point 40 links from *A* and 50 links from *C*, and pull the chain taut so that it lies on the ground in two straight lengths, *AD* and *CD*.

Drive in a stake at the point *D*.

The stakes *A*, *C* and *D* form a triangle whose sides are:

$$AC = 30 \text{ links,}$$
$$AD = 40 \text{ links,}$$
$$DC = 50 \text{ links.}$$

Now, according to the Egyptian rope-stretchers, the angle *DAC* is a right angle.

The line *DA* gives the direction of the goal-line through *A*. Set up a line of poles in the direction *DA* extending on both sides of *A*, and measure along it, on each side of *A*, one-half of 3 ch. 41 lk. (i.e. $\frac{1}{2}$ of 75 yards), that is, 1 ch. $70\frac{1}{2}$ lk. This gives the full length of the goal-line through *A*.

4. In the same way set out the goal-line through *B* and you will have the corners of the pitch, at each of which a stake should be driven in the ground.

5. Between the corners at each end of the pitch, set up lines of poles to indicate the position of the touch lines. The touch-lines and goal-lines can now be marked white in the usual way.

In setting-out the right angle *DAC* we chose as the lengths of the sides of the triangle, 30 links, 40 links, and 50 links. We might have chosen any other three lengths in the same proportion; that is, in the proportion of 3, 4, and 5.

For instance, 3 yards, 4 yards, and 5 yards. This was the secret which the Egyptian rope-stretchers knew.

Let us see if we can prove that such a triangle is really a right-angled triangle.

The following interesting geometrical puzzle will help us to do this.

Cut out of thin cardboard or thick drawing paper, two squares, sides 3 centimetres and 4 centimetres long.

Can you cut up these squares and rearrange the parts so as to form a single square?

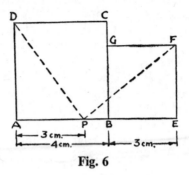

Fig. 6

In Fig. 6 are two squares, *GFEB* and *DCBA*, the lengths of the sides of which are 3 centimetres and 4 centimetres respectively. Show how to cut them up and rearrange them so as to form *one* square.

Measure *AP*, 3 centimetres long; this will leave *PE*, 4 centimetres long because the whole length of *AE* is 7 centimetres.

Cut along the dotted lines *PD* and *PF*, and so get three pieces of paper (or thin cardboard): the two right-angled triangles *PAD* and *PEF*; and the irregularly-shaped piece, *DPFGC*.

How can we rearrange these, so as to form one square?

We move the right-angled triangle *DAP* into the recess *FGC*. It will fit there because both *AP* and *GF* are 3 centimetres long.

Now move the right-angled triangle *FPE* so that *PE* fits against *DC*, both of which are 4 centimetres long.

This is what we now have: the figure *DPFQ*.

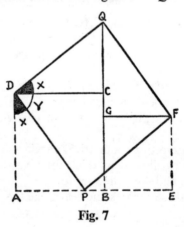

Fig. 7

Is this figure a square?

In order that it shall be a square, its sides must be all of the same length, and its angles must be right angles.

This is how we can see that these conditions are fulfilled: cut out a right-angled triangle exactly like the triangle *DAP*. It will be found that this triangle will fit exactly over the triangles *PEF*, *QGF*, *DCQ*. Therefore the sides *DP*, *PF*, *FQ* and *QD* are all the same length; that is, one of the conditions is fulfilled.

The angles marked *X* are equal, so the whole angle made up from the angles *X* and *Y* must be a right angle, for the angle *X* + the angle *Y*, regarded as the angle of the square *ABCD*, is a right angle; therefore, the angle *X* + the angle *Y*, regarded as an angle of the figure *DPFQ*, must be a right angle.

Therefore, the figure *DPFQ* is a square.

What is the area of this square?

It is clearly equal to the areas of the two squares *ABCD*, *BEFG*, with which we started.

$$\text{The square } ABCD = 16 \text{ square centimetres;}$$
$$\text{the square } BEFG = \underline{\ 9 \text{ square centimetres;}}$$

therefore,   the square *DPFQ* = 25 square centimetres;

therefore, the sides of the square *DPFQ* must be 5 centimetres.

Thus we see that the lengths of the sides of the triangle *DAP* are 3 centimetres, 4 centimetres and 5 centimetres.

This shows that the Egyptian rope-stretchers were justified in using a triangle whose sides are in the proportion, 3, 4, 5, for setting-out right angles.

A learned Greek, named Pythagoras, who was born in Asia Minor about 500 years before Christ was born, lived with a number of other learned men in a kind of college in the south of Italy. They spent their lives in study, and one of them—it is not known which—found that it is possible to make *any* two squares, no matter what are the lengths of their sides, into one square. This became known as the Theorem of Pythagoras.

One way to prove this theorem is exactly similar to the one we used in the case of the squares whose sides were 3 inches and 4 inches respectively.

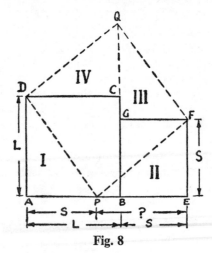

Fig. 8

Draw any two squares, and show how to cut them up so that the parts can be re-arranged to form one square.

ABCD, Fig. 8, is the larger of the two squares; in the diagram we have written the letter *L* to stand for " the length of the longer side ".

BEFG is the smaller square. In the diagram we have written the letter *S* to stand for " the length of the smaller side ".

We have used these letters merely as a kind of shorthand.

From the corner *A* of the larger square, measure *AP* equal to *S*. What will be the length of *PE*?

Now, the whole length from *A* to $E = L + S$;
But, from *A* to *P* $= S$;
therefore, the distance from *P* to *E* $= L$.

Thus, we see that we can cut off the right-angled triangle marked I and remove it to the position marked III, because *AP* and *GF* are equal, each being equal to *S*, the length of the side of the smaller square.

Similarly, if we cut along the line *PF*, we can move the right-angled triangle marked II to the position marked IV, because the lengths *PE* and *DC* are equal, each being equal to *L*, the length of the sides of the larger square.

By reasoning similar to that used in the case of the 3-4-5-triangle, as we may call it, we show that the figure *DPFQ* is a square; the length of the sides of this square is *DP*, which is called the *hypotenuse* of the right-angled triangle *DAP*.

Now let us cut out two squares exactly the same sizes as those in Fig. 8; namely *ABCD* and *BEFG*; we can fix these squares as shown below.

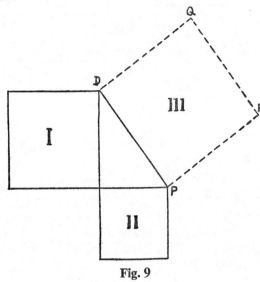

Fig. 9

We now see that,

Square I + Square II = Square III.

Square I may be called " the square on the perpendicular side " of the right-angled triangle *DAP*.

Square II may be called " the square on the base ".

Square III may be called " the square on the hypotenuse ", and so we get the usual form in which the theorem of Pythagoras is stated :

" In a right-angled triangle, the square on the perpendicular, plus the square on the base, equals the square on the hypotenuse."

This rule enables us to calculate the length of the hypotenuse of a right-angled triangle when we know the lengths of the other two sides.

Calculate the length of the hypotenuse of the right-angled triangle in Fig. 10. (Perpendicular = 12 ins.; base = 5 ins.)

N

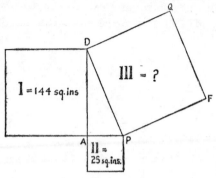

Fig. 10

The square on the perpendicular $=$ $12^2 = 144$ sq. ins.
The square on the base $=$ $5^2 = 25$ sq. ins.

Therefore, the square on the hypotenuse $= 12^2 + 5^2 = 169$ sq. ins.
Now, what is the length of side of a square whose area is 169 sq. ins.?
The process of finding the length of side of a square whose area is
known is called " Finding the Square Root ".

In the present case, by trial we find that $13^2 = 169$; therefore, the
length of the hypotenuse $= 13$ inches.

Square roots

Archimedes was the first to record the square root of a number;
that is, the length of side of a square of known area; the method
which, it is believed, he used is very simple, but before we examine
it we shall show how to find the area of a square in two ways; one
of which we know already.

What is the area of a square whose sides are 23 inches long?

I. Divide the square into two rectangles as shown in Fig. 11, one
20 inches broad, the other 3 inches broad.

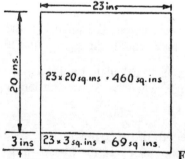

Fig. 11

The area of the first rectangle is 460 square inches; that of the second rectangle is 69 square inches; therefore the total area is 529 square inches.

II. Divide the square into three parts, one of which is a square whose sides are 20 inches long; the others rectangles, one 23 inches by 3 inches, the other 20 inches by 3 inches (Fig. 12).

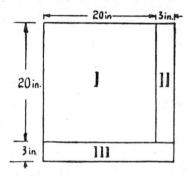

Fig. 12

$$23^2 = \text{Area I} + \text{Area II} + \text{Area III}.$$

Area I $= 20 \times 20$ sq. ins. $= 400$ sq. ins.
Area II $= 20 \times \ 3$ sq. ins. $= \ 60$ sq. ins.
Area III $= 23 \times \ 3$ sq. ins. $= \ 69$ sq. ins.

Therefore, the total area, namely $23^2 = 529$ sq. ins., as we found by the other method.

Pythagoras, several centuries before Archimedes, discovered the properties of certain sets of numbers.   One set,

$$1, 3, 6, 10, \ldots,$$

he called *triangular* numbers because these numbers of things can be arranged to form triangles, as follows:

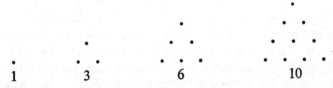

With a little thought you will be able to add to the list of triangular numbers. Try to write down, say, the next three triangular numbers after 10.

Another set,

$$1, 4, 9, 16, \ldots,$$

he called *square* numbers because these numbers of things can be arranged to form squares as follows:

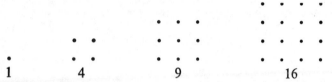

1   4   9   16

He noticed that any square number can be formed from a smaller square number by the addition of an ⌐-shaped border. Here we see two ways of forming the square number 25, from smaller square numbers and suitable ⌐-shaped borders. (The Greek called these ⌐-shaped borders, *gnomons*.)

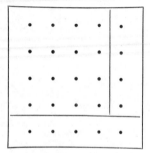

<table>
<tr><td>The small square:</td><td>The small square:</td></tr>
<tr><td>$4 \times 4 = 16$</td><td>$3 \times 3 = 9$</td></tr>
<tr><td>The gnomon:</td><td>The gnomon:</td></tr>
<tr><td>$4 \times 1 = 4$</td><td>$3 \times 2 = 6$</td></tr>
<tr><td>$(4+1) \times 1 = 5$</td><td>$(3+2) \times 2 = 10$</td></tr>
<tr><td>Total $= 25$</td><td>Total $= 25$</td></tr>
</table>

You will notice the close resemblance between these Pythagorean patterns of the square number 25 and the diagram on page 181. It was, no doubt, patterns and diagrams such as these that led Archimedes to the method of finding square roots. We shall now use the diagram-method of finding the square root of, say, 1156.

What is the length of the sides of a square whose area is 1156 square inches?

Draw a diagram, as Fig. 13, which consists of the square I and the rectangles II and III which are equal in width.

We have to determine the area of the square I, and of the rectangles II and III so that the combined areas shall be 1156 square inches.

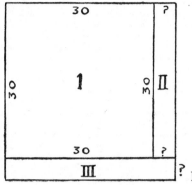

Fig. 13

The length of sides of the large square is greater than 30, because

$$30^2 = 900;$$

and less than 40 because

$$40^2 = 1600,$$

so we start with the side of the square I, 30 inches long. The combined areas of the two rectangles will be got by subtracting the area of square I, that is, 900 square inches, from 1156 sq. ins.

$$
\begin{aligned}
& 1156 \text{ sq. ins.}\\
- \; & 900 \text{ sq. ins.}\\
\hline
= \; & 256 \text{ sq. ins.}
\end{aligned}
$$

We must now find the width of the rectangles II and III, so that their combined areas shall be 256 square inches.

Since these two rectangles must be the same width, it will be more convenient to place them end-to-end as shown in Fig. 14, by moving rectangle II into the position IV, shown dotted. What must be the width of the rectangle made up of rectangles III and IV so that its area shall be 256 square inches?

The combined length of these two rectangles is greater than 60 inches, but we may make a rough estimate of the width by dividing 60 into 256. It goes about 4; so we now see that if we make the breadth 4 the total length of the rectangle made up of IV and III will be 64 inches.

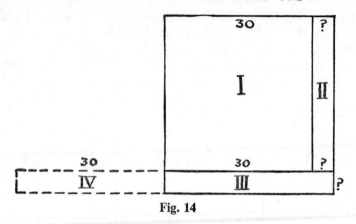

Fig. 14

Therefore, the area IV + area III = 64 × 4 square inches;
$$= 256 \text{ square inches};$$

therefore it is correct to take the breadth of these rectangles to be 4 inches. Therefore,

the length of sides of the large square = (30 + 4) inches
$$= 34 \text{ inches.}$$

Therefore, the square root of 1156 square inches = 34 inches.

EXERCISE XL

1. Describe, in your own words, how you would set-out, on a new housing estate, a new road at right angles to an existing road, by means of surveyor's poles and chain.

2. A one-acre square field contains 4,840 square yards. Show, by actual multiplication, that the length of the sides of the field is greater than 69 yards, but less than 70 yards.

3. Find the lengths of sides of squares containing these areas:
   (a) 625 square yards.
   (b) 361 square inches.
   (c) 729 square feet.
   (d) 1,024 square yards.

4. Calculate the length of the rafters for a roof whose span is 24 feet, and rise 9 feet.

Fig. 15

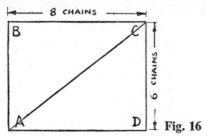

Fig. 16

5. The figure *ABCD* represents a rectangular field; *AC*, a foot-path (Fig. 16). Calculate the length of this foot-path.

6. How much shorter is the direct distance from *A* to *C* than the distance from *A* to *C* round the two sides *AB*, *BC*?

7. *AB* represents a saw-cut across a board, 12 inches wide. The point *B* is 16 inches from a point exactly opposite to the point *A* (Fig. 17). Calculate the length of the saw-cut.

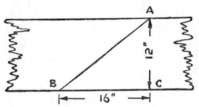

Fig. 17

8. Fig. 18 shows one of the rafters of a lean-to roof. Calculate its length.

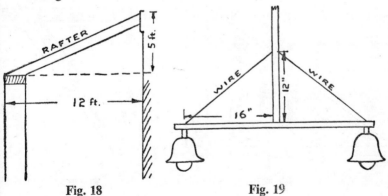

Fig. 18   Fig. 19

9. Fig. 19 represents a bracket for carrying two electric lights. Calculate the length of each sloping wire.

10. Fig 20 is a sketch of a wall-crane made from parts of a **Meccano** set. Calculate the length of the jib.

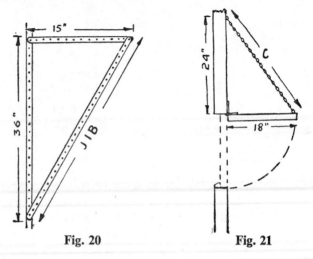

Fig. 20   Fig. 21

11. A chain is used to hold a heavy metal door in a horizontal position as shown in (Fig. 21). Calculate the length, C, of the chain from the dimensions given.

12. Fig. 22 represents a spandrel, that is, a panelled framework, fixed under a stair-case. Calculate the length, L, of the sloping piece.

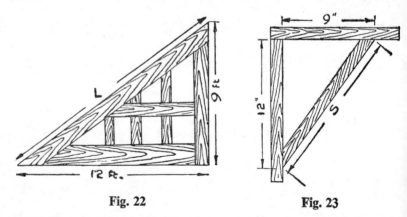

Fig. 22   Fig. 23

13. Calculate the length, S, of the sloping piece in this bracket (Fig. 23).

14. The mid-point D of the chord AB of a circle, centre C, radius 13 inches, is 5 inches from the centre of the circle. Calculate the length of the chord.

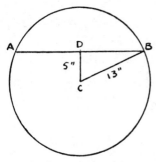

Fig. 24

15. T is a point, 26 inches from the centre C of a circle, 10 inches radius. PT is a tangent to the circle, that is, it is at right angles to the radius CP.

Calculate the length of the tangent PT.

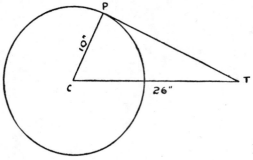

Fig. 25

16. $AEFG$ is a rectangle, 32 ft. × 8 ft. $ABCD$ is a square equal in area to this rectangle. Calculate (*a*) the length of the sides of the square, (*b*) the lengths of the lines BE and DG.

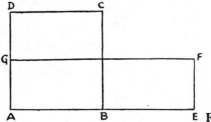

Fig. 26

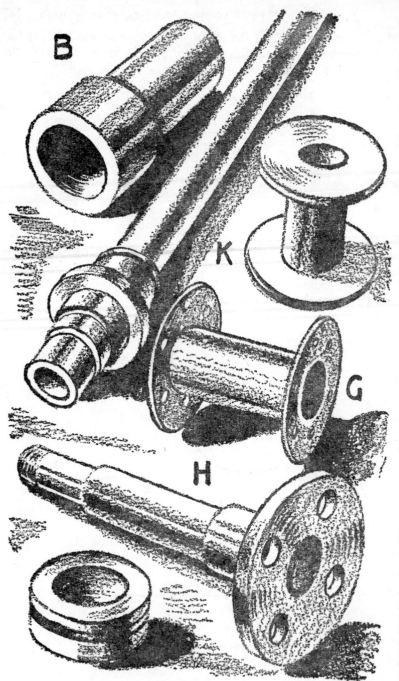

X

THE CIRCLE

Measuring diameters of circles

Metal things like those shown at *B, G, H, K*, in the illustrations opposite are made in engineering workshops by workmen called *turners*, who use machines called lathes. If you examine the piece marked *B*, you will see that the *diameter* at one end is greater than the diameter at the other end, and that at the end where the diameter is the greater a circular hole has been bored in it.

The turner works from a drawing something like this, on which all the necessary measurements are shown:

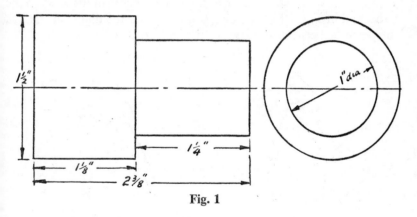

Fig. 1

He would be supplied with pieces of metal—aluminium, brass, iron, etc.—$1\frac{5}{8}$ inches diameter. These, one at a time, he would fix in the lathe and turn little by little from $1\frac{5}{8}$ inches diameter to $1\frac{1}{2}$ inches diameter along the whole length.

How is the turner to measure the diameter of the metal as the turning proceeds? He cannot measure with a ruler at the ends because of the way the piece is fixed in the lathe, so he uses an instrument called a pair of calipers. You will see a pair of calipers in Fig. 2. These are called outside calipers.

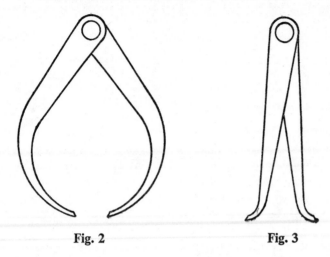

Fig. 2   Fig. 3

In Fig. 4, we see the turner testing the diameter of his work in the lathe, and in Fig. 5 he is reading from the ruler the diameter, that is, the distance between the jaws of the calipers.

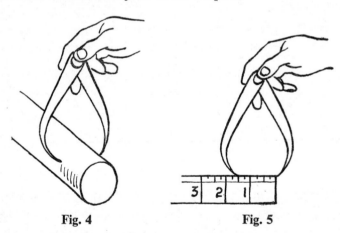

Fig. 4   Fig. 5

When the turner wants to measure the diameter of a hole such as that in the end of *B* of the illustration, he uses a pair of *inside* calipers (Fig. 3).

Sometimes we need to measure the diameter of a circle on a work-shop drawing. If the centre of the circle is shown on the drawing, the diameter of the circle may easily be found. Draw any line pass-

ing through the centre, and measure its length. This is the diameter.
If the centre of the circle is not marked on the drawing, this is how
we proceed.

Take any point *P* on the *circumference* of the circle, and using a
pair of compasses cut off two equal *chords*, *PQ*, *PR*, as shown in
Fig. 6.

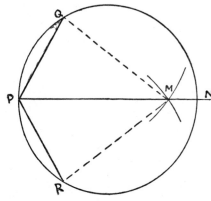

Fig. 6

First, with *Q* as centre, then with *R* as centre, and with the compasses set to any radius, draw two *arcs* of circles intersecting at *M*.
Join the point *P* to the point *M* and produce the line until it cuts the
circle at *N*. Measure the length of *PN*; this is the diameter of the
circle.

It is not difficult to see that the line *PN* is really a diameter of the
circle, because, if the paper on which the drawing has been done
were folded along the line *PM*, the triangle *PQM* would fit exactly
over the triangle *PRM*, and of course the part of the circle from *P*
through *Q* to *N* would fit exactly over the other part, from *P* through
R to *N*. So the line *PN* divides the circle into two equal parts;
therefore *PN* is a diameter of the circle.

It will be seen too, that the line *MP* divides the angle *QPR* into
two equal parts; that is, it *bisects* it. We might have bisected this
angle, as we did on page 151, by laying the ruler first along the line *PQ*
then along the line *PR* and drawing lines parallel to *PQ* and *PR*, and
joining the point where they cross to *P*. Try this and show that this
line is the same as the line *PM*.

Sometimes we need to find the diameter—or the radius—of a
circle of which only part of the circumference is given; for example,
a carpenter has to make a curved piece of wood (shaded in Fig. 7)

for a bricklayer who has to build an arch over a window opening in a wall. The bricklayer would tell the carpenter the width of the opening and the height of the middle point of the arch above height of the lower ends.

What is the radius of the circular arch, the dimensions of which are shown in Fig. 7?

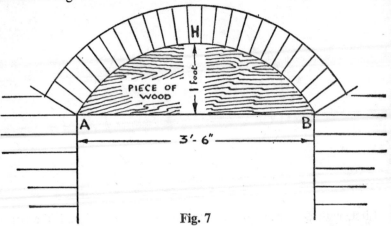

Fig. 7

Let us make a drawing of this window opening to a scale of 1 inch to represent 1 foot.

A and *B* will then be $3\frac{1}{2}$ inches apart; and *H* will be 1 inch above the middle of the line *AB*.

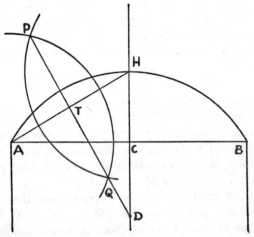

Fig. 8

We must find the centre of the circle passing through the points *A*, *H* and *B*. Since the point *H* is vertically above the mid-point *C* of the line *AB*, we say the line *HCD* " bisects the line *AB* at right angles ".

The centre of the circle must lie on the line *HCD*.

Join *A* to *H* and bisect this line at right angles; this is done by drawing two intersecting arcs, both having the same radius, one with *A* as centre, the other with *H* as centre. These arcs intersect at *P* and *Q*. Where the line joining *P* and *Q*, when produced, cuts the line *HCD* is the centre of the circle. The distance from *D* to *H* (or to *A*) is 2 inches. So the radius of the arch is 2 feet.

There is a method of calculating the radius of an arch from such dimensions as were given in the question above; this we shall do in Book Three.

A turner often has to find the centre of a circular disc or of the end of a cylindrical shaft. He cannot use the method which we have just used, so he uses a special tool for the purpose. It consists of two pieces of metal firmly jointed together at an angle, and a blade one edge of which, *BP*, bisects the angle *ABC* (Fig. 9).

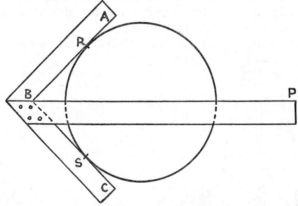

Fig. 9

The turner rests the blade on the disc and moves it until the edges *AB* and *BC* of the angular piece just touch the circumference of the circle. Then he scratches a line along the edge of the blade with a sharply pointed *scriber*. The scratch marks one diameter of the disc or end of the shaft. The tool is then turned into another position and another scratch is made along another diameter. Where these two diameters cross is the centre of the circle.

The reason why the blade of this tool shows the position of a diameter of the circle is this:

BA and *BC* are *tangents* to the circle. They touch the circle at the points *R* and *S*. Now, whenever two tangents are drawn to a circle from a point outside it you will find:

(i) their lengths are equal;

(ii) each tangent and the line joining the point where it touches the circle (called the point of contact) to the centre are at right angles to each other;

(iii) The line joining the centre of the circle to the point from which the tangents were drawn bisects the angle between the tangents. (This line, therefore, marks the position of a diameter of the circle.)

Measuring and calculating circumferences of circles

Milk bottles, jam jars and such like vessels are cylindrical; so a horizontal section of such an upright vessel is a circle.

Let us measure the circumference of, say, a milk bottle.

Take a strip of paper about 1 inch wide, and wrap it once round the bottle (Fig. 10). Where one end of the strip begins to overlap the other make a pencil mark. Unwrap the strip and place it by the edge of a ruler and so get the circumference.

The circumference of the pint bottle shown was 9·7 inches.

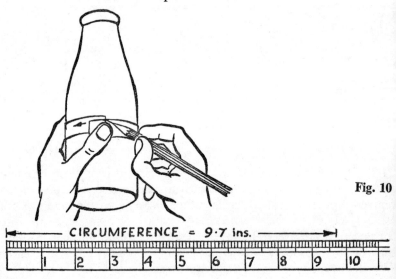

Fig. 10

Archimedes, of whom we heard when we were finding square roots, found a method of calculating the circumference of a circle from the diameter. He found that by dividing the circumference of a circle, no matter what the size of the circle, by the diameter he always got the same answer. Let us see what the answer would be in the case of the milk bottle.

Measure the diameter of the milk bottle with a pair of outside calipers, or if you cannot get calipers place the bottle lengthwise on a table between two blocks of wood, and measure the distance between the blocks (Fig. 11).

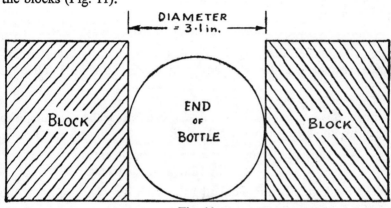

Fig. 11

The diameter of the milk bottle in Fig. 11 was 3·1 inches.

$$\frac{\text{Circumference}}{\text{Diameter}} = \frac{9\cdot7 \text{ ins.}}{3\cdot1 \text{ ins.}}$$

$$
\begin{array}{r}
3\cdot13 \text{ approx.} \\
3\cdot1 \overline{\smash{\big)}\,9\cdot7} \\
9\cdot3 \\
\hline
40 \\
31 \\
\hline
90 \\
\end{array}
$$

= 3·13 approximately.

In the case of a 3-lb. jam jar the measurements made in the same way were:

Circumference = 12·6 inches;
Diameter = 4 inches.

$$\frac{\text{Circumference}}{\text{Diameter}} = \frac{12\cdot6 \text{ ins.}}{4 \text{ ins.}}$$

= 3·15.

Archimedes, after a very long calculation, found that the *ratio* of the circumference to the diameter, is approximately $3\frac{1}{7}$. Let us change $\frac{1}{7}$ into a decimal, to the nearest hundredth, and compare our results with that of Archimedes.

$$\frac{1}{7} = \frac{100}{7} \text{ hundredths.}$$

14 hundredths, approximately.

7 ⟌ 100 hundredths

Therefore,

$$3\tfrac{1}{7} = 3\cdot14 \text{ approximately.}$$

Our result for the milk bottle was 3·13; a little below Archimedes' result: for the 3-lb. jam jar it was 3·15; a little above his result.

Thus, we may take the ratio to be 3·14.

From this we get two rules: one for calculating the circumference when we know the diameter. This rule is:

Circumference = $3\frac{1}{7}$ times the diameter, or,
3·14 times the diameter.

The other rule is for calculating the diameter when we know the circumference. This rule is:

Diameter = Circumference divided by $3\frac{1}{7}$, or
= Circumference divided by 3·14.

Let us test these rules, by applying them to the milk bottle and jam jar.

First. The diameter of a milk bottle is 3·1 inches. Calculate the circumference.

We shall work in decimals.

Circumference = 3·14 × diameter,
= 3·14 × 3·1 inches.

$$
\begin{array}{r}
3\cdot14 \times 3\cdot1 \\
\hline
9\cdot42 \\
\cdot314 \\
\hline
9\cdot734 \text{ inches}
\end{array}
$$

This result is approximately that which we got by measuring, namely, 9·7 inches.

Second. The circumference of a jam jar is 12·6 inches. Calculate the diameter.

Diameter = Circumference ÷ 3·14

$$= \frac{12 \cdot 6}{3 \cdot 14} \quad \left(\text{Approximate calculation is } \frac{12}{3} = 4 \right).$$

                    4 approx.
      314 ⟌ 1260
            1256
            ────
            4 remainder.

Therefore the diameter is 4 inches, approximately, which is what we got by direct measurement.

So we shall always use one or other of these two rules when we are dealing with diameters and circumferences of circles.

EXERCISE XLI

In the following examples, use either $3\frac{1}{7}$ or 3·14, as the ratio of the circumference of a circle to its diameter.

1. It was 50 yards round a circular paddling-pool. How many yards was it across?

2. The diameter of the barrel of an electric cable drum is 9 inches (Fig. 12). Calculate, to the nearest inch, its circumference. How many yards of cable would unwind from it in 18 revolutions? (Neglect the diameter of the cable itself.)

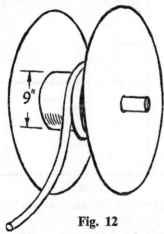

9″

Fig. 12

3. The barrel of a hauling machine is 6 inches in diameter. How far would it haul a ship in 20 revolutions?

4. The wheels of this bicycle are 20 inches in diameter. How **far** would the machine travel during one revolution of the wheels?

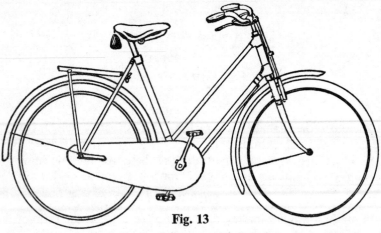

Fig. 13

5. How many revolutions of the wheels of the bicycle in Question 4 would it take to travel a mile?

6. Fig. 14 is a plan of a race-track. How many yards is it round the track?

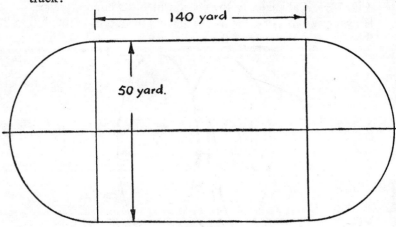

Fig. 14

7. How many times round the race-track in Question 6 would make approximately one mile?

8. An aeroplane flew round an aerodrome three times in a circle $2\frac{1}{2}$ miles diameter before landing. How many miles was that?

9. The diameter of the earth is approximately 8,000 miles. Calculate, to the nearest one-hundred miles, the distance round it at the equator.

10. The moon moves round the earth once every month, in a path which we may take to be a circle, half-a-million miles diameter (Fig. 15). How many miles does it travel in a month?

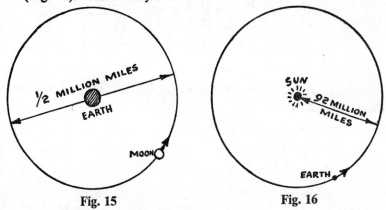

Fig. 15   Fig. 16

11. The earth travels round the sun, in a path which we may take to be a circle, 92 million miles radius, once every year (Fig. 16). How many million miles does it travel in a year?

12. A biscuit tin, 5·8 inches high, 3·6 inches diameter, was made out of a rectangular piece of sheet tin, 5·8 inches wide. Calculate the length of the rectangle, that is, the circumference, allowing 0·25 of an inch for overlap for the joint.

13. The diameter of a 2-lb. Golden Syrup tin is 3·4 inches. Its height is 4 inches. Calculate the dimensions of a rectangular piece of sheet metal needed to make such a tin, allowing 0·25 of an inch for the joint.

14. This cylindrical vat is to be made by bending, and riveting together, three plates of sheet metal. Calculate the circumference of the vat, and, allowing 1½ ins. overlap for riveting at each joint, the length of each plate.

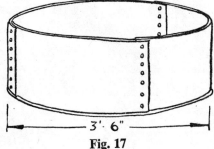

Fig. 17

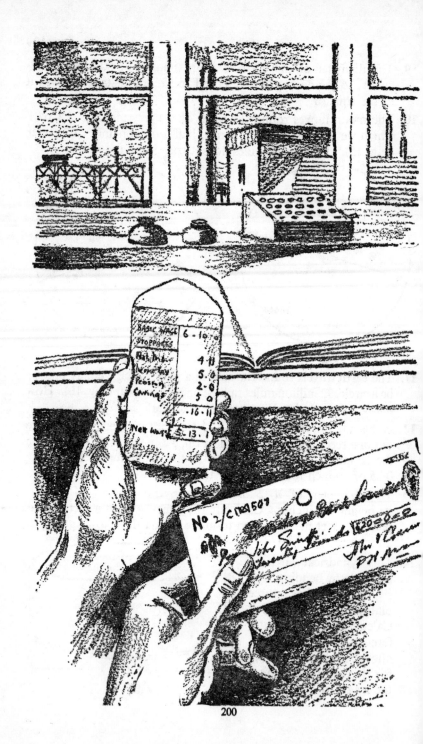

XI

WAGES AND SALARIES

WHAT is the difference between wages and salaries? Both are earnings for work done.

In most cases, wages, the earnings of workers, are paid weekly. Salaries, the earnings of officials and supervisors, are paid monthly. Domestic servants, however, are paid monthly as a rule, but their earnings are generally called wages.

Wages

The rates of wages of workers are of various kinds:

(1) There are " standing-wages " or " flat-rate-wages ". These are at a fixed rate per week, such as £5 per week, £3 17s. 6d. a week, and so on.

(2) There are " time-rate-wages " according to which the amount of wages depends upon the number of hours worked. For instance, an artisan may be paid at the rate of, say, 2s. 10½d. an hour for a normal week of 48 hours, 44 hours, or whatever has been agreed upon between the trade unions and the employers. If the worker works more than the number of hours in a normal week, he is paid for the extra hours " over-time " at a different rate; in some cases perhaps the extra hours are counted as " time-and-a-half "; in others as " double-time ". Suppose the normal week is 48 hours, and a man worked, in a certain week, 56 hours, and that the extra hours are reckoned as " time-and-a-half ", he would get paid as though he had worked 48 hours plus 1½ times 8 hours; that is, as though he had worked 60 hours.

(3) There are also " piece-rate-wages " according to which the amount earned depends upon the quantity of things made, or on the amount of work done.

For instance, a miner working at the coal-face may be paid at the rate of 12s. 6d. (or whatever it is) a ton for every ton of coal that he hews from it; a semi-skilled capstan-lathe operative in an engineering workshop may get, say, 1s. 6d. a dozen for the parts he produces;

or a girl machinist in a garment factory may get 4d. a dozen for her share of the work on a certain garment, and so on.

It sometimes happens that a " piece-rate " worker, through no fault of his own, is not continuously employed; the machine which he works may break down; or a garment-maker may not get materials as quickly as she needs them. Are such piece-workers penalized because of these defects? No, arrangements are usually made so that the workers shall not suffer hardship. They are paid at " time-rate " for their " idle-time ", and at piece-rates when they are producing things.

The examples in this chapter are mainly concerned with the multiplication and division of sums of money, large and small. If you have forgotten how to do these processes, you will find, on pages 245 and 249, the methods recommended, and on pages 246 and 250 some examples for practice.

Standing-wages

A man was paid at the rate of £4 13s. 6d. a week. How much would he earn in a year? (Reckon 52 weeks in a year.)

Amount earned in a year = £4 13s. 6d. × 52.

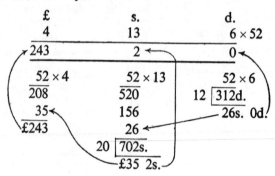

Amount earned in a year = £243 2s. 0d.

A domestic help was paid £6 7s. 9d. a month in addition to her board and lodgings. How much did she get (a) a week, (b) a year. (Reckon 4 weeks in a month, and 12 months in a year.)

$$\text{Amount received per week} = \text{£6 7s. 6d.} \div 4$$
$$= \text{£1 11s. } 10\tfrac{1}{2}\text{d.}$$

$$\text{Amount received per year} = \text{£ 6 7s. 6d.} \times 12$$
$$\overline{\text{£76 10s. 0d.}}$$

Time-rates

How much would a plumber earn in a normal week of 48 hours at the rate of 2s. 10½d. an hour?

Amount earned in a week = 2s. 10½d. × 48.

The quickest, and best, way of doing this multiplication is to deduct 48 times 1½d., that is 6s., from 48 times 3s., which is £7 4s.

The amount earned, therefore, is £6 18s.

Another way of working out 2s. 10½d. × 48 is this; note that 48 is 4 dozen, and that 2s. 10½d. is 34½d., then proceed as follows:

1 doz. @ 34½d. = 34s. 6d.,
so, 4 doz. @ 34½d. = 138s.
= £6 18s.

With a little practice, you should be able to reckon the wages due for a given number of hours' work, at a given rate per hour, as the workmen do it, namely, " in your head ", that is mentally.

A workman, however, does not find it necessary to make a lengthy calculation, even mentally, every time " pay-day " comes round. He knows from experience what his wage will be for a full week's work, then if he had worked any overtime he adds this to it, or if he had had any time off work, he deducts an amount from it.

For example.

We saw that the wage for a normal week of 48 hours at 2s. 10½d. an hour is £6 18s.

(i) How much should be deducted if a man had 3 hours off work?

Working " mentally " we should say, " three times 3s. is 9s.; three times 1½d. is 4½d., so 4½d. less than 9s. should be deducted: that is, 8s. 7½d.

The actual deduction from the week's wage would then be done as follows:

From £6 18s. deduct 9s., leaving £6 9s.; then adding 4½d. we should get £6 9s. 4½d. for 45 hours' work.

(ii) How much should be added for 8 hours' overtime at time-and-a-half rate?

8 hours' overtime at time-and-a-half rate is equivalent to 12 hours' extra time at 2s. 10½d. an hour.

12 hours, that is, 1 doz. hours @ 2s. 10½d. an hour = 34s. 6d.

Therefore the wage for a normal week's work plus 8 hours' overtime at time-and-a-half rate would be £8 12s. 6d.

The *wages-clerk* in the office of a works in which many of the workmen are paid time-rate wages has the job of reckoning the wages earned by those men, week by week. To lighten his task and to make sure that his calculations are right, he is supplied with a ready-reckoner.

Here is part of a ready-reckoner from which wages at rates ranging from 1s. 9d. an hour to 2s. 3d. an hour, for hours per week from 40 to 50 can easily be calculated.

Nr. of Hrs.	Rate per Hour						
	1/9	1/10	1/11	2/-	2/1	2/2	2/3
40	£3/10/-	£3/13/4	£3/16/8	£4/-/-	£4/3/4	£4/6/8	£4/10/-
41	3/11/9	3/15/2	3/18/7	4/2/-	4/5/5	4/8/10	4/12/3
42	3/13/6	3/17/-	4/-/6	4/4/-	4/7/6	4/11/-	4/14/6
43	3/15/3	3/18/10	4/2/5	4/6/-	4/9/7	4/13/2	4/16/9
44	3/17/-	4/-/8	4/4/4	4/8/-	4/11/8	4/15/4	4/19/-
45	3/18/9	4/2/6	4/6/3	4/10/-	4/13/9	4/17/6	5/1/3
46	4/-/6	4/4/4	4/8/2	4/12/-	4/15/10	4/19/8	5/3/6
47	4/2/3	4/6/2	4/10/1	4/14/-	4/17/11	5/1/10	5/5/9
48	4/4/-	4/8/-	4/12/-	4/16/-	5/-/-	5/4/-	5/8/-
49	4/5/9	4/9/10	4/13/11	4/18/-	5/2/1	5/6/2	5/10/3
50	4/7/6	4/11/8	4/15/10	5/-/-	5/4/2	5/8/4	5/12/6

This is how the ready-reckoner is used.

Suppose we wish to find the wage for 47 hours at 1/10 an hour; we look for the amount among those on the same line as 47 hours; the rate per hour, namely, 1/10, is found at the top of the second column, so we take the amount given in that column, namely, £4/6/2.

Thus,   47 hours @ 1/10 an hour = £4/6/2.

Similarly,   43 hours @ 2/3 an hour = £4/16/9.

You see from this how the wages-clerk's task is lightened, and the chance of his making mistakes reduced.

Piece-rates

During a week, a miner hewed the following amounts of coal:

Monday	1 ton 2 cwts.	Thursday	1 ton 10 cwts.
Tuesday	19 cwts.	Friday	1 ton 12 cwts.
Wednesday	1 ton 8 cwts.		

How much did he earn at 25s. a ton?

The total amount of coal hewn is 6 tons 11 cwts., that is, $6\frac{1}{2}$ tons plus 1 cwt.

$$6\frac{1}{2} \text{ tons at 25s. a ton} = £1 \text{ 5s.} \times 6\frac{1}{2}$$
$$= £7 \text{ 10s. plus 12s. 6d.}$$
$$= £8 \text{ 2s. 6d.}$$
$$1 \text{ cwt. @ 25s. a ton} = \quad 1\text{s. 3d.}$$

Therefore, he would earn £8 3s. 9d.

A machinist in a hosiery factory was paid at the piece-rate of 1s. $1\frac{1}{2}$d. a dozen seams. This was her output during one week:

Monday	$10\frac{1}{2}$ doz.
Tuesday	$12\frac{1}{2}$ doz.
Wednesday	11 doz.
Thursday	$13\frac{1}{2}$ doz.
Friday	$14\frac{1}{2}$ doz.
Saturday	6 doz.

How much did she earn during that week?

$$\text{Total output} = 68 \text{ dozen.}$$

68 doz. @ 1s. $1\frac{1}{2}$d. per doz. $= 68$s. plus 68 times $1\frac{1}{2}$d.
$$= £3 \text{ 8s. plus 8s. 6d. (because there}$$
$$\text{are eight three-half-pences in}$$
$$\text{1 shilling)}$$
$$= £3 \text{ 16s. 6d.}$$

A wages-clerk would use a ready-reckoner for finding earnings at piece-rates.

The ready-reckoner on page 204 could be used for finding the earnings at rates, varying from 1/9 each, or per dozen, to 2/3 each, or per dozen, of numbers of things from 40 to 50. More complete ready-reckoners, containing a large range of prices and numbers of things, can be bought in most bookshops. Such books are much used in workshops and offices.

Salaries

Salaries are usually reckoned at such-and-such an amount per annum; say, £250 per annum, £320 per annum. They are usually paid in equal monthly instalments, or in equal quarterly instalments.

A junior clerk was engaged at a salary of £195 per annum. What would be the equivalent weekly income from this. (Reckon 52 weeks in a year.)

$$\text{Income per week} = £195 \div 52.$$

```
            £3           15s.           0d.
    ────────────────────────────────────────
    52 │ £195            0s.            0d.
         156           780s.
        ────           ─────
         £39       52 │ 780
                       52
                      ────
                       260
                       260
                      ────
```

Therefore, the equivalent income per week is £3 15s. 0d.

A post was advertised at a commencing salary of £250 per annum with annual increment of £15. Maximum salary £400 per annum.

Calculate (i) the income per week from this commencing salary;
        (ii) the increase, or increment, per week;
      (iii) the number of years before the maximum, or highest salary, that is £400 per annum, will be reached.

(i) Income per week of commencing salary = £250 ÷ 52.

```
            £4           16s.           2d. nearly
    ──────────────────────────────────────────────
    52 │ £250            0s.            0d.
         208           840s.           96d.
        ────           ─────           ────
         £42       52 │ 840        52 │ 96
                       52              52
                      ────            ────
                       320            44d. remainder.
                       312
                      ────
                        8s.
```

Therefore, income per week at commencing salary is £4 16s. 2d. nearly.

(ii) Increase per week at the end of each year = £15 ÷ 52.

```
                 5s.              9d. approximately
   52 │ £15       0s.              0d.
                 300s.            480d.
            52 │ 300        52 │ 480
                 260             468
                 40s.            12d. remainder.
```

Therefore, the increase per week at the end of each year is 5s. 9d.

(iii) Total increase in salary from the commencing salary to the maximum or highest salary is £400 – £250 = £150.

Increase per annum = £15.

Therefore, the number of years to reach the maximum salary
= 10.

EXERCISE XLII

Calculate, mentally, the following:

1. 48 hours @ 2/1 an hour.
2. 48 hours @ 1/11 an hour.
3. 36 hours @ 1/9 an hour.
4. 36 hours @ 2/1 an hour.
5. 36 hours @ 2/3 an hour.
6. 36 hours @ 1/11 an hour.
7. 47 hours @ 2/3 an hour.
8. 45 hours @ 2/6 an hour.
9. 44 hours @ 1/10 an hour.
10. 39 hours @ 1/7 an hour.
11. 40 hours @ 2/3 an hour.
12. 50 hours @ 2/1 an hour.
13. 49 hours @ 1/10½ an hour.
14. 47 hours @ 1/10½ an hour.
15. 49 hours @ 1/11 an hour.
16. 37 hours @ 2/6 an hour.
17. 49 hours @ 2/3 an hour.
18. 39 hours @ 2/11 an hour.
19. 30 hours @ 2/1 an hour.
20. 38 hours @ 2/7 an hour.

Find the following by means of the ready-reckoner on page 204:

21. 42 hours @ 2/3 an hour.
22. 49 hours @ 1/11 an hour.
23. 45 hours @ 2/1 an hour.
24. 50 hours @ 1/10 an hour.
25. 47 hours @ 1/9 an hour.
26. 41 hours @ 2/3 an hour.
27. 46 hours @ 1/10 an hour.
28. 50 hours @ 1/11 an hour.
29. 49 hours @ 1/10 an hour.
30. 40 hours @ 1/11 an hour.

31. Which is the higher rate: £4 16s. a week or £235 per annum?

32. A man worked 6 hours overtime, at time-and-a-half rate. His time-rate of pay was 2/2 an hour for a normal week of 44 hours. How much did he earn that week?

33. Calculate the week's wages of a man who worked a normal week of 44 hours @ 2/2 an hour, plus 8 hours overtime at time-and-a-half rate.

34. Calculate the week's wages of a man who worked a normal week of 46 hours @ 2/3 an hour, plus 12 hours overtime at time-and-a-half rate.

35. Calculate the week's wages of a man who worked a normal week of 44 hours at 2/7 an hour, plus 10 hours overtime at time-and-a-half rate.

36. Calculate the net annual income of a man who worked 44 hours a week at 2/10 an hour, after deduction of 5/1 per week for National Insurance contributions.

37. How much pay should a workman receive after deduction for National Insurance of 5s. 1d. per week, for a normal week's work of 46 hours at half-a-crown an hour.

38. What is the equivalent weekly income from a salary of £300 per annum (52 weeks in a year)?

39. A man, earning a salary of £300 per annum, was paid quarterly, (that is, every 13 weeks). How much should he receive after deductions for National Insurance at the rate of 5s. 1d. per week, at the end of each quarter?

40. A post was advertised as follows:

Initial Salary,	£300 per annum;
Annual Increments,	£25 per annum;
Maximum Salary,	£600 per annum.

How much would the salary be at the beginning of the fifth year? How much would each of his monthly instalments of this salary be, after deducting National Insurance contributions at the rate of 5s. 1d. per week?

41. A catering officer was appointed at a salary of £550–£610 per annum, paid monthly.

Calculate the monthly salary, after deduction of National Insurance of 5/1 per week,

    (*a*) at the minimum of £550 per annum,

    (*b*) at the maximum of £610 per annum.

42. This is an extract from an advertisement: " Wanted, One Deputy Matron—State Registered Nurse—salary £130 to £210 by annual increments of £15 per annum, plus £100 per annum living-out allowance if non-resident."

Calculate the equivalent total monthly income from this post for a non-resident Deputy Matron during the first year and during the second year.

XII

AT THE TOWN HALL

THE Town Hall is the centre where most of the business of the Corporation is carried on. In it one usually finds the offices of the various paid officials of Corporation: the Borough Treasurer, who controls the money matters of the town; the Borough Engineer or Surveyor, who deals with buildings, roads, water supply, etc.

The Town Councillors, who are elected by the ratepayers, do not receive any payment: they give their services free.

How does a Corporation get the money needed to carry on its activities?

The answer is: " Mainly from the rates."

Here are some particulars compiled by the Borough Treasurer of a certain town for his own use, and for the information of the Town Councillors, which will help us to understand how the town's affairs are carried on.

AREA OF THE TOWN (in acres)		10,580
POPULATION	Total	101,553
	School Children	11,939
RATEABLE VALUE OF THE PROPERTY IN THE TOWN		£1,596,709
NET YIELD OF A 1d. RATE		£6,653
RATE LEVIED IN THE BOROUGH		9s. 1d.

EXPENDITURE OF THE CORPORATION'S COMMITTEES:

Highways	£257,000
Education	186,000
Baths	22,870
Parks	53,406
Cleansing	80,697
Watch Committee (for Police)	46,572
Other Committees	249,449

The area of the town

The first piece of information given in the particulars on page 211 is intended to convey some idea of the size of the town. To a farmer or to a person living in the country the term *acres* conveys a very definite idea. Such persons are accustomed to hear of a farm of 100 acres, of 350 acres; of a field of 2½ acres, 12 acres, and so on.

So far, in this book, acres have only been mentioned once: on page 184. There it was merely stated that 1 acre is equal to 4,840 square yards, and we were able to grasp the size of an acre by calculating the number of square yards in two squares:

(i) the sides being 69 yards, the area is 4,761 sq. yds.,
(ii) the sides being 70 yards, the area is 4,900 sq. yds.,

from which we saw that an acre is larger than a square those sides are 69 yards in length, and less than a square whose sides are 70 yards in length.

Another way of expressing the size of a district is in square miles.

Let us therefore try to find the relation between acres and square miles.

$$1 \text{ mile} = 1,760 \text{ yds.}$$

so, $$\qquad 1 \text{ sq. ml.} = 1,760 \times 1,760 \text{ sq. yds.}$$

$$
\begin{array}{r}
1,760 \\
1,760 \\
\hline
1,760,000 \\
1,232,000 \\
105,600 \\
\hline
3,097,600 \\
\end{array}
$$

Therefore, $\qquad$ 1 sq. ml. = 3,097,600 sq. yds.

Now, $\qquad$ 1 acre = 4,840 sq. yds.

therefore, $\qquad$ 1 sq. ml. $= \dfrac{3,097,600}{4,840}$ acres.

$$
\begin{array}{r}
640 \\
4,840 \overline{)3097600} \\
29040 \\
\hline
19360 \\
19360 \\
\hline
0 \\
\end{array}
$$

Therefore, $\qquad$ 1 square mile = 640 acres.

You will find it useful to commit to memory the following facts about acres, square yards and square miles:

$$1 \text{ acre} = 4{,}840 \text{ square yards.}$$
$$640 \text{ acres} = 1 \text{ square mile.}$$

Let us return to the area of the town given on page 211.
Express the area of the town, given on page 211, in square miles.

$$\text{Area in acres} = 10{,}580$$
$$\text{Area in sq. ml.} = \frac{10{,}580}{640}$$
$$= \frac{1058}{64}$$

$$
\begin{array}{r}
16 \\
64\ \overline{)\ 1{,}058} \\
64 \\
\hline
418 \\
384 \\
\hline
34
\end{array}
$$

Therefore,   the area $= 16\frac{1}{2}$ square miles approximately
                          $= 16\cdot5$ square miles approx.

Now the boundaries of a town are usually very irregular. The town in question is a seaside town, so one boundary is the seashore, which is fairly straight, and approximately 7 miles long.

The area of the town being approximately $16\cdot5$ square miles, and its length along the seashore or promenade being 7 miles, calculate the average width of the town inland from the shore.

$$\text{Total area} = 16\cdot5 \text{ sq. ml.}$$
$$\text{Length of town} = 7 \text{ miles.}$$

Therefore, the average width of the town inland $= \dfrac{16\cdot5}{7}$ miles
                          $= 2\cdot4$ miles,
                          approximately.

Thus the town covers as much ground as a rectangle 7 miles by $2\cdot4$ miles, so the boundaries of the town are approximately

$$2(7 + 2\cdot4) \text{ miles long} = 2(9\cdot4) \text{ miles long}$$
$$= 18\cdot8 \text{ miles long}$$

EXERCISE XLIII

Where necessary, use the particulars relating to the Corporation's affairs given on page 211.

1. Calculate the average number of people in the town, per square mile.

2. Calculate the total expenditure of all the committees.

3. How much is the total expenditure of all the committees per head of the population?

4. What is the cost per head of the population for the following services:

    > Highways,
    > Education,
    > Baths,
    > Parks?

5. How much per head of the population does the Police Force cost?

Here are some particulars relating to the three Ridings of Yorkshire in a certain year for use in Questions 6 to 12 inclusive:

Riding	Area	Population
East	736,024 acres	200,110
North	1,354,391 acres	340,431
West	1,610,829 acres	1,504,057

6. Calculate the area of the East Riding in square miles.

7. Calculate the area of the North Riding in square miles.

8. Calculate the area of the West Riding in square miles.

9. Calculate the density of the population in the East Riding, in persons per square mile.

10. Calculate the density of the population in the North Riding, in persons per square mile.

11. Calculate the density of the population in the West Riding, in persons per square mile.

12. From your results in Questions 5 to 11, complete the following
table, arranging the Ridings in order of descending density of
population, that is, place the most densely populated area at the
top of the list.

Riding	Density of Population
1.	
2.	
3.	

13. In a certain year the total expenditure of all the committees of
the Birmingham Corporation was £6,848,000. The population
of the city was then 1,076,000. Calculate the cost per head of
the population.

14. Here are some particulars relating to City of Oxford and the
County Borough of Cambridge in a certain year:

	Population	Total Expenditure
Oxford	103,570	£813,800
Cambridge	80,160	£684,520

Calculate the expenditure per head of the population in Oxford
and in Cambridge.

15. From the particulars on page 211, calculate the expenditure on
cleansing per head of the population.

16. In a certain year the total expenditure on education in Burton-
on-Trent was £104,800. The population was 48,690. Calculate
the cost of education per head of the population.

17. Here are some particulars relating to Buckinghamshire and
Leicestershire for a certain year:

County	Population	Total Expenditure
Buckinghamshire	368,500	£1,483,000
Leicestershire	327,300	£1,037,000

Calculate the expenditure per head of population in each of those two counties.

18. In a certain year the Cardiff Corporation spent £1,889,000 on its services. The population was 230,630.
Calculate the expenditure per head of the population of the city.

19. In a year when the expenditure of the City of Sheffield was £3¾ million, the estimated population of the City was 508,370. Calculate the expenditure per head of the population.

20. In a certain year the estimated population of Bournemouth was 116,797. The total expenditure of the town in that year was £721,900. Calculate the expenditure per head of the population.

The rateable value and rates

Every piece of property in a town, except churches and schools, has what is known as a RATEABLE VALUE. This is an amount which depends upon the rent of the property, but is always less than the annual rental. This Rateable Value is fixed by a Government Valuation Officer, according to rules laid down in an Act of Parliament. This Act of Parliament is rather too difficult for you to understand at present, but you will learn about it in a later book of this series.

The rateable value of the whole of the properties in a town is called " The Rateable Value of the Town ".

This is a very simple basis for calculating the income of a Corporation.

We saw, on page 211, that the Rateable Value of the town to which the particulars shown there relate, was £1,596,709.

We also saw among those particulars an item called " The Net Yield of a 1d. Rate ", the amount of which was £6,653.

Now, what does this mean?

It means that if the rates were 1d. in every £ of the Rateable Value of the whole of the property of the borough or town, the income of the corporation would be £6,653.

Let us see if this is correct.

The total Rateable Value of the property in the town is £1,596,709; therefore the income from a 1d. rate would be 1,596,709 pence. We shall convert this into £s to the nearest £.

The simplest way to do this is to divide by 240, because there are 240 pence in £1.

£6,653 nearly

240 | 1596709 pence
    1440
    ‾‾‾‾
    1567
    1440
    ‾‾‾‾
    1270
    1200
    ‾‾‾‾
     709 (this remainder is nearly three
times 240).

Therefore, when we know the Rateable Value of a town in £s, we can calculate the yield of a 1d. rate from it.

Then, if we know how much the rates in the £ are, we can calculate the income of the Corporation from the rates.

For instance, the Rateable Value of a town was £785,260, and the rates were 8s. in the £.

Calculate the total income of the corporation of that town from the rates.

The Rateable Value = £785,260;

therefore,

the yield of a 1d. rate = 785,260 pence

Working
£3272

240 | 785260 pence
   720
   ‾‾‾
   652

= £3,272 nearly.

   480
   ‾‾‾‾
   1726
   1680
   ‾‾‾‾
    460

Therefore, the income

from a rate of 8s. in £ = £3,272 × 96 (because there are 96 pence in 8s.)

= £314,112.

Working
3272 × 96
‾‾‾‾‾‾‾‾‾
294480
 19632
‾‾‾‾‾‾‾
314112

EXERCISE XLIV

1. Here is a table showing the rateable values of several towns in England in a certain year:

Name of Town	Rateable Value of Town	Yield of a 1d. Rate
Bath	£610,014	
Bedford	£367,827	
Birmingham	£7,199,226	
Blackpool	£1,596,709	
Bradford	£2,184,268	

Calculate the yield of a 1d. rate in each of these towns, and so complete the table.

2. How much would a rate of one shilling in the £ yield in Bath?

3. In a certain year the rates in Blackpool were 9s. 1d. in the £. Calculate the total income, during that year, from the rates.

4. From the particulars given on page 211, we saw that the yield of a 1d. rate was £6,653.
Calculate the number of pence in the £ in the rates to cover the cost of each of the following services:

Education; Parks; Highways.

5. The Baths Committee of a certain town estimated that it would need £20,000 during a certain year. The Rateable Value of the town was £540,726. How many pence in the £ would be needed on the rates to cover this expenditure?

6. The Publicity Committee of a seaside town was allowed to spend on advertisements the proceeds of a rate of ½d. in the £. The rateable value of the town was £255,100. How much was the committee allowed?

7. In a certain year the Rateable Value of Sheffield was £3,865,000. Calculate the yield of a 1d. rate in that year.

Calculate the amount of rates to be paid in respect to each of the properties in questions 8 to 20 inclusive.

	Rateable Value of the Property	Rates in the £
8.	£35	12s. 6d.
9.	£120	15s. 4d.
10.	£68	9s. 5d.
11.	£52	16s. 1d.
12.	£265	13s. 4d.
13.	£96	22s. 3d.
14.	£28	11s. 7d.
15.	£45	19s.
16.	£135	12s. 10d.
17.	£88	8s. 4d.
18.	£76	23s. 6d.
19.	£125	13s. 7d.
20.	£96	17s. 6d.

XIII

AT THE POST OFFICE

WE are all familiar with the local post office. It is there that we buy postage stamps, post letters, and send telegrams; but do we all realize that it is a branch of, perhaps, the oldest, certainly one of the largest, businesses in the country?

It is not known when the Government, on behalf of the King, began to " carry letters " for the people; but there is reason to believe that it was before 1516—that is, when King Henry VIII was king—that the first " Master of the Posts " was appointed.

The fact that the wages-bill for the people employed by the Post Office is about £100 million, shows it must be a very large concern.

In the post offices in towns there are grills on the counters, and on these grills are notices to tell the public the kind of business that is transacted in different parts of the office:

> Stamps, Telegrams, Registered Letters and National Insurance Stamps.
> Postal Orders, Money Orders, Savings Bank and National Savings Certificates.
> Wireless and other Licences.
> Pensions and Allowances.

Postage rates

A very convenient way to buy stamps is in small books which contain 6 @ 2½d.; 6 @ 2d.; and 6 @ ½d.

The cost of such a book is half-a-crown, because, one of each kind of these stamps would cost 5d.; therefore six of each kind would cost 6 times 5d., that is, 2s. 6d.

On the inside of the cover of one of these books of stamps there is some useful information. Here is a copy of it. From time to time Postal Rates for letters, parcels, telegrams, etc., are changed. You should check the rates given on page 222 with the current rates, which you will find in diaries and at the post offices, and work all the examples with the current rates.

INLAND

LETTERS—First 2 oz. - - - - - 2½d.
   Each additional 2 oz. - - - - - ½d.
POSTCARDS - - - - - - - 2d.
PRINTED PAPERS—First 4 oz. - - - 1½d.
   Each additional 2 oz.; Max. 2 lb. - - - ½d.
NEWSPAPERS (Regd. at G.P.O.)
   First 4 oz. (per copy) - - - - - 1½d.
   Each additional 4 oz. (per copy); Max. 2 lb. ½d.
Newspapers may be sent as Printed Papers whether
registered or not.

The charges for parcels, not shown above are as follows:

Not over 3 lb. -	- 11d.	Not over 6 lb. -	- 1s. 5d.
„ „ 4 lb. -	- 1s. 1d.	„ „ 7 lb. -	- 1s. 6d.
„ „ 5 lb. -	- 1s. 3d.	„ „ 8 lb. -	- 1s. 7d.

From 8 lb. to 15 lb. (Weight limit) - 1s. 8d.

The charges for telegrams are:

First twelve words   -   1s. 6d.
Every additional word -   - 1½d.

Letters and parcels

What should be the postage on a letter, 7 oz. in weight?

For the first two ounces the charge is 2½d.
The charge for the remaining 5 ounces is 1½d.
Therefore, the total charge should be 4d.

What should be the postage on a package of newspapers (sent as printed papers) weighing 10½ ounces?

For the first four ounces the charge should be 1½d.
For the remaining 6½ ounces it should be 4 times ½d., that is, 2d.; therefore, the total charge should be 3½d.

What should be the postage on a parcel weighing 13 lb. 10 oz.?

Since the weight is greater than 8 lb. and less than 15 lb., the postage should be 1s. 8d.

Registered letters and parcels

Letters and parcels containing important documents, postal orders, money or other valuable things, should be sent by Registered Post. For this there is a minimum extra charge of 4d., called the Registration Fee.

The counter clerk who deals with Registered Letters and Parcels gives a receipt to the sender and takes charge of the letter or parcel. Registered Letters are never put in a pillar box or other posting box.

If a Registered Letter or Parcel on which the Registration Fee of 4d. has been paid is lost or damaged, compensation up to £5 may be claimed from the Post Office.

By payment of higher registration fees, compensation for loss or damage up to £400 may be claimed, according to the following scale:

For a registration fee of 5d. maximum compensation is £20: for every additional 1d. in the registration fee, the maximum compensation is increased by £20.

What is the maximum compensation claim that can be made in respect of a letter or parcel lost or damaged on which a registration fee of 10d. has been paid?

The maximum claim in respect of 5d. fee = £20; additional fee paid is 5d., so additional compensation claim = £100.

Therefore, the maximum claim when a registration fee of 10d. has been paid is £120.

A parcel will not be accepted for Registered Post unless the knots on the string, with which it is fastened, be sealed with sealing wax or other material.

Telegrams

What should be the charge for the following telegram?

" SMITH
  18 LORNE AVENUE
   MICKLEHAMPTON

SUCCESSFUL INTERVIEW   HAVE ACCEPTED POST COMMENCING EIGHTEENTH   NEXT MONTH
                              JAMES "

In this telegram there are 15 words.

Charge for the first 12 words is 1s. 6d.
Charge for the remaining 3 words is 4½d.
Total charge is 1s. 10½d.

Postal Orders

Although money, such as £1 and 10s. notes and a limited number of coins, may be sent by Registered Post, it is better to send it either in the form of Postal Orders, or by means of a Money Order.

Postal Orders are issued for amounts of 6d. to 21s. at nearly all post offices in the United Kingdom. This is what a Postal Order looks like:

(Reproduced by permission of H.M. Postmaster General).

The Post Office makes a small charge, called the *poundage*, for every Postal Order that is issued.

At the top left-hand corner of the Postal Order you will see a picture of the King's head and round this the words

" Postal Order Poundage "

Below this, it says

" ONE PENNY ".

Thus, the poundage on this 6d. Postal Order is 1d., therefore the cost of it is 7d.

Here is the list of poundage charges:

On orders for 6d. and 1s.	-	-	-	1d.
On orders from 1s. 6d. to 5s.	-	-	-	1½d.
On orders from 6s. to 21s.	-	-	-	2d.

What would be the charge for a Postal Order for 17s.?

The poundage charge would be 2d., so the total cost would be 17s. 2d.

How does a person get cash for a Postal Order that he has received?
He should take it to any post office, sign his name on the line at the bottom of the order where it says "signature" and hand it in to the counter clerk. He will then receive the money for the Order.

Money Orders

The safest way of sending money, especially large sums of money, through the post is by means of Money Orders. It costs a little more to send a Money Order than to send Postal Orders for the same amount, because of the extra work that has to be done by the post office staff.

Here is a copy of a Money Order form:

Stamp of Office	REQUEST FOR **INLAND MONEY ORDER**			No.	
	PLEASE FILL IN THIS FORM IN BLOCK CAPITAL LETTERS				
	FOR	£	s.	d.	Payment is required :- at the Post Office named below through a Bank by Telegraph (STRIKE OUT INSTRUCTIONS NOT REQUIRED)
PAYABLE TO	Mr., Mrs.or Miss	Christian Name (or Initials)		Surname	
PAYABLE AT	....POST OFFICE				
NAME AND ADDRESS OF SENDER	....				

(Reproduced by permission of H.M. Postmaster General).

Suppose you wish to send, say, £12 5s. 10d. by Money Order to a firm in Liverpool for some goods that you wish to buy. You should get a form like the one illustrated above, and fill in, in the spaces provided:

 (i) the amount, £12 5s. 10d.,
 (ii) the name of the post office in Liverpool where the order is to be cashed by the firm, say,

G.P.O. LIVERPOOL.

(iii) the name of the firm,

MESSRS. GOODALLS LTD.

(iv) your own name and address.

When you have done this, you should hand it to the counter-clerk together with the money, £12 5s. 10d., plus the charge—in this case it would be 10d., as you will see from the list of charges below.

The counter-clerk then enters on a similar form the details, except the name of the sender, which you have written on the form which you handed in, at the same time, by means of a piece of carbon paper, making a copy.

The clerk will give you one copy, which you should send by ordinary post to Messrs. Goodalls Ltd., and will send the other copy on which will appear the name of the sender to the G.P.O. Liverpool.

It now remains for Messrs. Goodalls Ltd. to collect the money. They should take the form which you sent to them to the G.P.O. Liverpool. The counter-clerk will ask the question:

" Who is the sender? "

If Goodalls Ltd. give them the correct name of the sender, then the counter-clerk will pay to them the amount on the order, namely, £12 5s. 10d.

Money Order Charges.

Amounts up to £10 - - - 8d.
Every additional £10 up to £50 - 2d.
" See the table."

(Maximum) 1s. 4d.

National Savings

Here are some extracts from a leaflet, issued by the Postmaster-General, which can be got at any Post Office. They contain information relating to the

Post Office Savings Bank,
National Savings Certificates,
National Savings Stamps.

POST OFFICE SAVINGS BANK

Opening an Account. Anyone over seven years of age may open an account with 5/- or more at any Post Office which transacts Savings Bank business. A depositor may hold more than one account. Accounts may be opened on behalf of children under seven years of age.

NATIONAL SAVINGS CERTIFICATES

The Certificates now on sale are the 9th issue, price 15/– per Unit
Certificate. Each Certificate held for ten years becomes worth 20/3;
the annual yield over the whole ten years' period being £3 0s. 11d.
per cent FREE OF INCOME TAX.

Purchase. National Savings Certificates can be purchased at most
Post Offices.

Repayment. Repayment of Certificates with accrued interest may
be obtained at short notice on application to the Director. Repayment application forms may be obtained at most Post Offices.

NATIONAL SAVINGS STAMPS

National Savings Stamps may be purchased at most Post Offices.
Stamp Savings Books containing sixty spaces in which Savings
Stamps can be affixed are supplied free of charge.

National Savings Stamps are intended to provide facilities for
enabling children and others who cannot save more than a small
amount at a time to accumulate sums of money to be used:—

1. To make deposits in a Savings Bank account.
2. To buy National Savings Certificates.

S A V E ★ R E G U L A R L Y

Here are some extracts from another pamphlet on National
Savings Certificates, from which the value of each Unit Certificate—
bought for 15s.—and held for any period less than ten years, may be
found.

THE FIRST EXTRACT

National Savings Certificates—NINTH ISSUE

RATE OF GROWTH.—At the end of the first year each unit in-
creases in value by 3d. During the second year $\frac{1}{2}$d. is added at the
end of each completed period of two months. During the third,
fourth, fifth, sixth and seventh years 1d. is added at the end of each
completed period of two months. Thereafter 1$\frac{1}{2}$d. is added at the
end of each completed period of two months until the end of the
tenth year, making 20/3 in all (See the table, reproduced overleaf).
This represents a rate of compound interest of £3 0s. 11d. per cent
per annum over the whole period of ten years.

In the third line from the end of this extract, it says:

" See the table."

This piece of advice is very necessary, because it is not at all a
simple calculation, to find the value from this first extract. The table
reproduced overleaf, makes the matter perfectly clear.

Q   D.L.M.

THE SECOND EXTRACT

NINTH ISSUE

On Completion of	1st Year s. d.	2nd Year s. d.	3rd Year s. d.	4th Year s. d.	5th Year s. d.	6th Year s. d.	7th Year s. d.	8th Year s. d.	9th Year s. d.	10th Year s. d.
1st month	15 0	15 3	15 6	16 0	16 6	17 0	17 6	18 0	18 9	19 6
2nd ,,	15 0	15 3½	15 7	16 1	16 7	17 1	17 7	18 1½	18 10½	19 7½
3rd ,,	15 0	15 3½	15 7	16 1	16 7	17 1	17 7	18 1½	18 10½	19 7½
4th ,,	15 0	15 4	15 8	16 2	16 8	17 2	17 8	18 3	19 0	19 9
5th ,,	15 0	15 4	15 8	16 2	16 8	17 2	17 8	18 3	19 0	19 9
6th ,,	15 0	15 4½	15 9	16 3	16 9	17 3	17 9	18 4½	19 1½	19 10½
7th ,,	15 0	15 4½	15 9	16 3	16 9	17 3	17 9	18 4½	19 1½	19 10½
8th ,,	15 0	15 5	15 10	16 4	16 10	17 4	17 10	18 6	19 3	20 0
9th ,,	15 0	15 5	15 10	16 4	16 10	17 4	17 10	18 6	19 3	20 0
10th ,,	15 0	15 5½	15 11	16 5	16 11	17 5	17 11	18 7½	19 4½	20 1½
11th ,,	15 0	15 5½	15 11	16 5	16 11	17 5	17 11	18 7½	19 4½	20 1½
12th ,,	15 3	15 6	16 0	16 6	17 0	17 6	18 0	18 9	19 6	20 3

Certificates of the Ninth Issue may be retained for 10 years from the date of purchase.

The following examples will show you how this table is used.

1. A National Savings Unit Certificate was bought on May 4th in a certain year. How much would it be worth on September 16th in the third following year?

The interval of time from May 4th in one year to May 4th in the third following year is 3 years; to September 4th in that year, 3 years and 4 complete months. Since the interval from September 4th to September 16th is less than a complete month it is neglected.

The value will be found in the column headed 3rd Year, on the line which starts on the left with 4th Month. The amount is 15s. 8d.

2. A National Savings Unit Certificate was bought on November 10th in a certain year. How much would it be worth on June 1st in the sixth year following?

The interval of time from November 10th in one year to November 10th in the *fifth* following year is 5 years.

The interval from November 10th in the fifth following year to May 10th in the sixth following year is 6 months. The rest of the time, that is, from May 10th to June 1st is less than one complete month, so it is neglected.

Therefore the complete time interval is 5 years 6 months.

The value will be found in the 5th-year column, on the 6th-month line: that is, the value is 16s. 9d.

3. 10 National Savings Unit Certificates were bought for a baby on the day it was born, namely, July 15th in a certain year. How much would they be worth on October 20th in the year when the child was 7 years old.

The interval is 7 years 3 months 5 days. Neglect the 5 odd days.

The amount will be found in the 7th-year column, on the 3rd-month line: that is, the value of each unit certificate is 17s. 7d.

Therefore 10 Certificates would be worth 17s. 7d. × 10 = £8 15s. 10d.

National Insurance contributions

In general, everyone living in Great Britain over school age is insurable in one of three classes:

Class I. Employed persons; that is, those who work for wages or salary.

Class II. Self-Employed persons; that is, persons in business on their own account.

Class III. Non-Employed persons; that is, everyone not in either Class I or Class II.

MAIN RATES OF WEEKLY CONTRIBUTIONS

CLASS 1 (EMPLOYED PERSONS)

	MEN			WOMEN		
Age	Paid by Employee	Paid by Employer	Total	Paid by Employee	Paid by Employer	Total
18 and over	5s. 1d.	4s. 4d.	9s. 5d.	4s. 0d.	3s. 5d.	7s. 5d.
Under 18	2s. 11½d.	2s. 6½d.	5s. 6d.	2s. 5d.	2s. 0d.	4s. 5d.

CLASS 2 (SELF-EMPLOYED PERSONS)

MEN		WOMEN	
18 and over	6s. 6d.	18 and over	5s. 5d.
Under 18	3s. 9d.	Under 18	3s. 3d.

CLASS 3 (NON-EMPLOYED PERSONS)

MEN		WOMEN	
18 and over	5s. 0d.	18 and over	4s. 0d.
Under 18	2s. 11d.	Under 18	2s. 5d.

Contributions are paid by means of stamps—National Insurance Stamps—which can be bought only at a post office.

Single stamps for the total amount of the insurance contribution are fixed to a card.

Contributors in Class I must have their cards stamped by the employer; those in Classes II and III must buy their own stamps and fix them to their cards.

What prices of stamps are needed for the following:

(i) A domestic servant, 17 years old;
(ii) An engineering apprentice, 19 years old?

Licences

The following Licences—and many others—are to be obtained at any Postal Money Order Office, at the prices shown:

Wireless Receiving Licence - - £1
Dog Licence - - - - - 7s. 6d.
Motor Cars - - - - - £12 10s. per annum
  (Quarterly licences are issued at 27½% of the annual licence for the quarters beginning 1st Jan.; 25th Mar.; 1st Jul.; 1st Oct.)
Gun Licence - - - - - 10s.

Pensions and allowances

Retirement Pensions:

Men over 65 and insured
women over 60 -   -   -   30s. a week
Wives over 60 -   -   -   -   20s. a week
Widows under 60 -   -   -   26s. a week

Family Allowances (for children under sixteen years of age):

For every child in a family after
the first   -   -   -   -   5s. a week
For the first child of a widow -   7s. 6d. a week

EXERCISE XLV

Information needed in the following questions will be found on pages 222 to 231 inclusive.

1. What change should you get out of a ten-shilling note after paying postage on the following:

Letters: 3 oz.; 5 oz.; $8\frac{1}{2}$ oz.
Parcels: 3 lb. 6 oz.; 7 lb. 4 oz.; $4\frac{1}{4}$ lb.?

2. How much would it cost for the following stamps:

Postage Stamps: 30 @ $2\frac{1}{2}$d.; 2 doz. @ 2d.; 75 @ 1d.; 110 @ $\frac{1}{2}$d.
National Insurance Stamps: 12 @ 9s. 5d.; 28 @ 7s. 5d.; 35 @ 4s. 5d.?

3. How much would it cost for the following Postal Orders (including the poundage):

2 @ 2s. 6d.; 1 @ 8s. 6d.; 1 @ 15s.?

4. How much would it cost for Postal Orders to the value of £3 18s. 6d. (including poundage)?

5. How much would it cost to send £5 15s.

      (*a*) by Postal Order and Registered Letter?
      (*b*) by Money Order and ordinary post?

6. What would be the Registration Fee to cover compensation for loss or damage up to the following amounts:

£60; £100; £75; £125; £340; £250?

7. A parcel weighing 7 lb. 4 oz. worth £15, was sent by parcel post, registered to cover completely its worth in case of damage or loss. How much would this cost?

8. What would be the maximum that could be claimed for the loss of a package containing jewellery if the registration fee paid was 6d.?

9. How much would it cost to send the following telegram:

" JONES
    AVONDALE
        26 MYRTLE AVENUE
           SOUTHWICH

    I ARRIVED SAFELY AT 9.15 P.M. I FOUND UNCLE VERY ILL BUT DOCTOR SAYS HE WILL BE ABLE TO TRAVEL AT THE END OF MARCH
                        SAMUEL "?

10. Redraft the telegram in Question 9 so as to convey the same information at less cost.

11. Suppose you have arrived safely at the school camp on the Vicarage Farm, Pytchley, Northamptonshire. Draft a telegram to your mother telling her of your safe arrival and giving her your address. The telegram is to cost not more than 1s. 6d.

12. What would be the value of the following National Savings Certificates:

(*a*) One Unit Certificate, bought on January 16th, cashed on May 1st in the 3rd following year?

(*b*) Five Unit Certificates, bought on June 30th, cashed on January 1st in the 5th following year?

(*c*) Ten Unit Certificates, bought on December 10th, cashed on November 1st in the 8th following year?

13. How much would it cost an employer per week for National Insurance for the following employees:

5 men, 1 apprentice (16 years old), 7 women, and 3 girls (ages 15, 17 and 19 years)?

14. What would be the total deductions from wages of the employees in Question 13 that the employer would be entitled to make?

15. How much would it cost for National Insurance stamps for the employees in Question 13?

16. A grocer, in business on his own account, forgot to stamp his National Insurance card for 3 weeks. How much would it cost him to bring his card up-to-date?

17. How much would the Family Allowance be for a family of 4 children under 16 years old?

18. A widow had three children under sixteen. How much a week would she be entitled to for her widow's pension and the allowances for her family?

19. Calculate

    (a) the cost of a quarterly motor car licence;

    (b) the difference between the cost of an annual licence and that of four separate quarterly licences;

    (c) the saving—when a car is not used during the Jan.–Mar. quarter—of taking out three separate quarterly licences instead of the full annual licence.

20. You were asked to buy at the post office licences for your dog, and for the wireless, and 1 dozen of each of the following stamps: 3d., 2½d. and 2d. How much money would you need?

21. A man and his wife received Retirement Pensions under the National Insurance Scheme. How much would they have per annum for other expenses if their rent came to 9s. 6d. a week?

22. How much a year does it cost a carpenter, in business on his own account, for contributions under the National Insurance Scheme?

23. How much a year would it cost a woman who earns her livelihood as a dressmaker working in her own home for contributions under the National Insurance Scheme?

24. Under the National Insurance Scheme sickness benefits are paid at the standard weekly rate of 26s. for a man, together with 7s. 6d. a week for the first child. He would also be entitled to draw Family allowances for any other children in his family. How much a week would a man with 3 children under sixteen years old, during sickness, be entitled to draw altogether?

SPECIAL CHAPTER
FOR
REFERENCE, REVISION
AND
SPEED PRACTICE

Addition

There is no arithmetical operation so important in everyday life as addition; it is, therefore, very necessary that we cultivate habits of accuracy and speed in addition.

How are we to acquire these habits?

Here are three suggestions that will help:

(i) Practice the " Look-and-Say " method.

Examples.
$$
\begin{array}{cccc}
3 & 5 & 4 & 7 \\
\underline{6} & \underline{2} & \underline{5} & \underline{3} \\
\rule{0pt}{1em} & & & \\
\text{—} & \text{—} & \text{—} & \text{—}
\end{array}
$$

In working these examples, do not say: " 6 *and* 3 *make* 9 ",
" 2 *and* 5 *make* 7 ",
" 5 *and* 4 *make* 9 ",

and so on; but merely *look* at the 6 and the 3, and *say* " 6, 9 "; look at the 2 and the 5, and say " 2, 7 " and so on.

If you are adding a column of digits as

$$
\begin{array}{c}
7 \\
2 \\
5 \\
4 \\
\underline{3} \\
\text{—}
\end{array}
$$

point to each digit in turn beginning either at the bottom or at the top of the column, and say—if you start at the bottom: 3, 7, 12, 14, *21*; and write the answer, 21.

If you start at the top and descend the column, say: 7, 9, 14, 18, *21*; the answer.

(ii) Build-up tens.

Examples.
$$
\begin{array}{cccc}
5 & 7 & 5 & 6 \\
\underline{9} & \underline{18} & \underline{26} & \underline{37} \\
\rule{0pt}{1em} & & & \\
\text{—} & \text{—} & \text{—} & \text{—}
\end{array}
$$

In the first example, mentally build-up 9 into 10 by taking **1** from 5, and we say 14.

In the second example, build-up 18 to 20 by taking 2 from **7**, and say, 25.

In the third example, build-up 26 to 30 by taking 4 from 5, and say 31.

In the fourth example, build-up 37 into 40 by taking 3 from 6 and say 43.

(iii) If possible, add as a whole ten, any groups of digits that make 10.

For instance,

$$
\begin{array}{r}
7 \\
3 \\
8 \\
5 \\
6 \\
\underline{5} \\
\overline{}
\end{array}
$$

In this column of digits there are two 5s which make 10; these may added as a whole ten; there are also 7 and 3 which make 10.

Start adding from the bottom upwards; add first, the two 5s which make 10, and then return to the 6 which lies between them and get 16; from this point proceed as follows:

$$16, \quad 24, \quad 34;$$

(say 34 after 24 because the 7 and 3 at the top of the column make 10 which is added as a whole).

Or, starting from the top, say:

$$10, \quad 18, \quad 28, \quad 34.$$

The following example will supply further practice. It should be done several times, starting first at the bottom, and then checked by starting at the top.

$$
\begin{array}{r}
2,627 \\
593 \\
8,418 \\
1,385 \\
276 \\
\underline{3,485}
\end{array}
$$

EXERCISE A

Addition

1.

7	4	4	9	2	5	9	5
5	3	8	2	6	5	4	8
3	8	3	3	8	7	3	2
2	7	2	5	5	2	6	3
1	2	5	4	4	3	4	9
6	5	7	7	7	6	1	7
6	5	5	6	2	2	5	2
2	8	4	2	1	2	7	2

2.

64	84	25	59	85	38
23	56	79	73	73	27
37	92	12	28	87	55
55	25	62	65	26	73
72	76	85	41	48	46
83	47	37	87	22	37

3.

748	695	6,259	3,582	8,607
67	484	473	1,264	4,359
365	528	1,482	7,958	7,184
295	211	5,678	943	2,426
523	573	3,735	6,275	1,753

In the following additions of money, make-up, as you proceed, the pence into shillings, and the shillings into £s. For instance, in the first, starting from the bottom of the pence column, say, " 9d., 1/3, 1/11, 2/3, 2/8. Put down 8d. and carry 2/–, and so on.

4.

£	s.	d.		£	s.	d.		£	s.	d.
3	10	5		19	5	10		65	9	4
2	16	4		26	13	4		85	11	7
5	3	8		18	12	7		14	3	5
6	17	6		35	9	2		52	17	8
4	18	9		29	11	5		17	4	6

5.

£	s.	d.	£	s.	d.	£	s.	d.
374	16	10	526	5	8	285	11	3
429	13	5	238	17	7	361	4	11
465	9	8	79	12	11	816	19	4
711	10	6	419	18	2	624	8	8
407	7	9	289	9	9	753	15	5

Subtraction

There are three ways of doing subtraction, all of which, when understood and practised, give good results. If you can do subtraction, stick to the method you know; if you cannot, here is some advice on one of the methods. You will easily understand it, and with practice, will no doubt become skilful in using it.

Usually the problem of subtraction is stated in this way: From one quantity take another quantity; for example, from 126 take 68. We shall put it another way: how many do we need to make 68 up to 126? This is the way a shopkeeper gives change to a customer.

Here is an example.

What change should you get out of a ten-shilling note, after spending 6s. 10d.?

The shopkeeper would go to her till, and take out 2d. from the coppers, and would probably say to herself " that makes seven shillings "; then she would take out 3s. from the silver and say to herself " ten shillings ".

Then she would go to the customer and say " 6s. 10d. ", and putting 2d. into your hand, " and 2d. makes 7s. "; then, putting 3s. into your hand, " and 3s. make 10s. ".

Thus she would have given you 3s. 2d. change.

We may call this method " The method of making-up "; some people call it by another name, a rather high-sounding name, " the method of complementary addition ".

You are advised to do all the subtractions in EXERCISES B and C by the " making-up method ".

Start by doing questions in Exercise B mentally, that is, do the working in-your-head, and just write down the answers in your exercise book.

EXERCISE B

In each of the following questions, you are to find the change out of either a ten-shilling note or a £1 note, after spending the amount given in the second line.

	s.	d.	s.	d.	s.	d.	s.	d.	s.	d.
1.	10	0	10	0	10	0	10	0	10	0
	8	10	7	11	5	9	8	7	4	5

	s.	d.	s.	d.	s.	d.	s.	d.	s.	d.
2.	10	0	10	0	10	0	10	0	10	0
	3	3	5	8	4	4	7	2	2	10

	s.	d.	s.	d.	s.	d.	s.	d.	s.	d.
3.	10	0	10	0	10	0	10	0	10	0
	5	$10\frac{1}{2}$	8	$9\frac{1}{2}$	4	$2\frac{1}{2}$	6	$6\frac{1}{2}$	3	$4\frac{1}{2}$

	s.	d.	s.	d.	s.	d.	s.	d.	s.	d.
4.	10	0	10	0	10	0	10	0	10	0
	2	7	7	$5\frac{1}{2}$	4	$1\frac{1}{2}$	8	5	2	$3\frac{1}{2}$

	£	s.	d.	£	s.	d.	£	s.	d.	£	s.	d.
5.	1	0	0	1	0	0	1	0	0	1	0	0
		18	10		16	4		13	8		12	2

	£	s.	d.	£	s.	d.	£	s.	d.	£	s.	d.
6.	1	0	0	1	0	0	1	0	0	1	0	0
		3	9		15	2		7	7		14	$9\frac{1}{2}$

	£	s.	d.	£	s.	d.	£	s.	d.	£	s.	d.
7.	1	0	0	1	0	0	1	0	0	1	0	0
		18	$3\frac{1}{2}$		12	7		2	$9\frac{1}{2}$		5	$7\frac{1}{2}$

	£	s.	d.	£	s.	d.	£	s.	d.	£	s.	d.
8.	1	0	0	1	0	0	1	0	0	1	0	0
		2	8		15	3		10	2½		7	9½

	£	s.	d.	£	s.	d.	£	s.	d.	£	s.	d.
9.	1	0	0	1	0	0	1	0	0	1	0	0
		16	8½		12	1½		7	6½		9	7½

	£	s.	d.	£	s.	d.	£	s.	d.	£	s.	d.
10.	1	0	0	1	0	0	1	0	0	1	0	0
		13	4		16	8		12	7		10	5

Subtraction (continued)

Let us now return to ordinary numbers.

The simplest subtraction sums are like these:

78	89	54	67	95
16	24	13	31	42

In these we are to make up the number on the lower line into that on the upper line.

In the first we should say: " 6 and 2 make 8 ", and as we say " 2 ", we should write 2 under the 6, that is in the units place. Then we should say: " 1 and 6 make 7 ", writing down the 6 in the tens column. The answer is therefore 62.

In the next, we say: " 4 and 5 make 9 ", writing down the 5 as we say it; then, " 2 and 6 make 8 ", writing down the 6 as we say it.

Thus the answer is 65.

In the same way do the remaining three subtractions.

The next type is that where we are to make-up to a given number of tens or hundreds, or thousands, and so on. Here are three examples:

60	500	8,000
14	143	2,356

In the first, we should say: " 4 and 6 make 10 ", writing down the 6 as we say it. Since we made the units column up to 10 we have one ten to carry. Now, dealing with the tens column, we say " 2 and 4 make 6 ", and write down 4 in the tens column. Therefore the answer is 46.

In the next, we say, " 3 and 7 make 10: write down 7 and carry 1 (to the next column); 5 and 5 make 10: write 5 and carry 1 (to the next column); 2 and 3 make 5: write down 3 ". Therefore the answer is 357.

In the third, the working would be: " 6 and 4 make 10: write down 4 and carry 1; 6 and 4 make 10: write down 4 and carry 1; 4 and 6 make 10: write 6 and carry 1; 3 and 5 make 8: write down 5." The answer is therefore 5,644.

Here are five more examples for practice:

80	400	6,000	700	73,000
34	263	1,827	638	11,294
—	—	—	—	—

The last type of example will be clear from the following:

$$635$$
$$148$$
$$—$$

Here we make-up the 8 in the units column to 15: we shall have 1 to carry to the tens column; then we make-up the 5 tens into 13 tens; thus we shall have 1 to carry to the hundreds column; finally, we have to make-up 2 to 6 in the hundreds column. Let us do the whole working aloud, writing down the figures which we stress or underline.

" 8 and 7, 15; carry 1: 5 and 8, 13; carry 1: 2 and 4, 6." Answer 487.

For practice, do the following:

43	524	6,173	18,711	5,281
19	267	2,539	3,769	1,396
—	—	—	—	—

We now conclude with an ordinary subtraction involving money.

£	s.	d.
83	10	3
17	18	9

Again, let us do the working aloud, writing down the numbers that we stress or underline. "9d. and 6d., 1s. 3d.; carry 1s.: 19s. and 11s., £1 10s.; carry £1: 8 and 5, 13; carry 1: 2 and 6, 8." Therefore, the answer is £65 11s. 6d.

Do these for practice:

£	s.	d.		£	s.	d.		£	s.	d.
46	2	10		528	13	5		602	1	3
27	15	11		164	18	9		194	8	8

EXERCISE C

Subtraction

1.

17	15	29	26	14	25	33	15	17	22	31
9	8	8	9	9	6	8	7	7	9	5

2.

34	52	75	37	93	71	62	48	65	44	56
18	37	58	19	64	23	49	29	38	17	27

3.

271	583	327	811	743	962	755	427	916	731	486
188	176	99	123	467	385	88	139	309	227	178

4.

s.	d.		s.	d.		s.	d.		s.	d.		s.	d.		s.	d.
1	0		1	0		1	0		1	0		1	0		1	0
	10			7			$6\frac{1}{2}$			$4\frac{1}{2}$			$10\frac{1}{2}$			$2\frac{1}{2}$

5.

s.	d.		s.	d.		s.	d.		s.	d.		s.	d.		s.	d.
2	6		2	6		2	6		2	6		2	6		2	6
	9			7		1	10			$9\frac{1}{2}$		1	$11\frac{1}{2}$		1	$3\frac{1}{2}$

6.

s.	d.	s.	d.	s.	d.	s.	d.	s.	d.	s.	d.
10	0	10	0	10	0	10	0	10	0	10	0
3	7	2	9	5	$6\frac{1}{2}$	2	$10\frac{1}{2}$	3	$7\frac{1}{2}$	1	$11\frac{1}{2}$

7.

£	s.	d.	£	s.	d.	£	s.	d.	£	s.	d.
1	0	0	1	0	0	1	0	0	1	0	0
	17	6		13	10		2	7		14	$3\frac{1}{2}$

8.

£	s.	d.	£	s.	d.	£	s.	d.	£	s.	d.
5	2	10	7	15	3	6	5	5	8	12	7
1	17	3	2	18	9	1	5	6	3	17	$10\frac{1}{2}$

9.

£	s.	d.	£	s.	d.	£	s.	d.	£	s.	d.
527	13	7	182	5	2	628	15	10	365	8	6
208	18	9	76	4	10	229	15	11	176	12	7

10.

lb.	oz.	lb.	oz.	lb.	oz.	lb.	oz.
7	0	3	0	6	2	10	4
1	12	1	10	2	14	3	9

11.

ft.	ins.	ft.	ins.	ft.	ins.	ft.	ins.
6	0	10	4	18	6	27	5
1	9	3	11	6	$10\frac{1}{2}$	13	$8\frac{1}{2}$

Multiplication (ordinary numbers)

If one number is to be multiplied by another, the second number is called the multiplier; the first number, the multiplicand. For example, in $3{,}256 \times 263$, 263 is the multiplier; 3,256 the multiplicand.

It is customary to write the multiplier below the multiplicand, as follows:

$$3{,}256 \times$$
$$\underline{263}$$

There are two ways of completing the working of this sum.

Some people start multiplying by the units digit in the multiplier, that is, by the 3; others start by multiplying by the digit on the extreme left of the multiplier; in the above case, by the 2, which of course stands for 200; the second method is the better for many reasons as we shall see later, so we recommend all to adopt it.

The working would then be set out as below:

$$
\begin{array}{r}
3{,}256 \times \\
263 \\
\hline
651\ 200 \\
195\ 360 \\
9\ 768 \\
\hline
856{,}328 \\
\hline
\end{array}
$$

Multiplication (money)

You are advised to set down the working of a multiplication of a sum of money like this:

Example. Multiply   £26   13s.   8d. by 46
            £1227   8s.   8d. Answer

46 ×	46 ×	46 ×
26	13	8
920	460	12 368 pence
276	138	30s. 8d.
31	30	
£1227	20 628s.	
	£31 8s.	

Procedure: (i) In the pence, shillings, and £s columns (in this order), multiply 46 by 8 (pence); 46 by 13 (shillings); 46 by 26 (£).

(ii) Change 368 pence into shillings and pence; that is, into 30s. and 8d. Put the 8d. above, in the place reserved for the answer, and transfer the 30s. to the shillings column, as shown by the arrow.

(iii) Change 628s. into £ and shillings; that is, into £31 8s.
Put the 8s. in the answer, and transfer the £31 to the £s column as shown by the arrow.

(iv) Add the £s and put the total in the answer.
Thus, £26 13s. 8d. × 46 = £1,227 8s. 8d.

EXERCISE D
Multiplication

1.
23	37	42	63	75
16	18	25	37	68

2.
134	245	365	438	528
45	57	69	76	94

3.
2,462	3,261	6,535	9,749
127	108	236	597

4.
3,027	5,328	8,476	7,964
209	728	1,507	3,728

5.

s.	d.		s.	d.		s.	d.		s.	d.
7	5		18	4		9	10		12	8
	9			7			5			8

6.

s.	d.		s.	d.		s.	d.		s.	d.
14	7		16	11		9	10		18	9
	13			23			35			68

7.

£	s.	d.		£	s.	d.		£	s.	d.
5	12	10		15	17	9		27	8	11
		35				49				58

8.

£	s.	d.		£	s.	d.		£	s.	d.
63	9	11		58	17	9		75	14	8
		67				29				96

9.

£	s.	d.
16	19	4
		32

£	s.	d.
42	12	7
		61

£	s.	d.
68	17	3
		89

10.

£	s.	d.
27	8	5
		65

£	s.	d.
38	12	9
		25

£	s.	d.
79	13	10
		84

Division

The process of division will be understood from the following simple example, in which the whole of the working is shown:

Divide 385 by 4.

$$\begin{array}{r} 96 \\ 4\,\overline{)385} \\ 36 \\ \hline 25 \\ 24 \\ \hline 1 \text{ remainder.} \end{array}$$

Let us say aloud all that we have done and set down in this example.

(i) 4 into 3? It won't go. 4 into 38: 9.

(ii) 9 fours = 36. Write down 36, and subtract it from 38. It leaves 2. Bring down the 5.

(iii) 4 into 25: 6.

(iv) 6 fours = 24. Write down 24, and subtract it from 25. It leaves 1.

Therefore, the answer is 96 and 1 remainder.

We could have done a lot of the working of this example "in-our-heads". In this way:

Remembering how we did subtraction, by the *making-up* method, we might have said, instead of line (ii),

"9 fours = 36: and *2* make 38" (stressing the *2* and writing it under the 8). Bring down the 5.

Then, instead of line (iv), we might have said,

"6 fours = 24: and *1* make 25" (stressing the *1* and writing it under the 5).

Setting it down, it would look like this:

$$
\begin{array}{r}
96 \\
4\ \overline{)385} \\
25 \\
\overline{1}\ \text{remainder.}
\end{array}
$$

In such a simple sum as this, you will probably consider it unnecessary to write down even the small amount of working shown in this second way of doing it. We need not, for instance, write down the 2 under the 8, and bring down the 5.

The working would then appear thus:

$$
\begin{array}{r}
96 \\
4\ \overline{)385} \\
1\ \text{remainder.}
\end{array}
$$

We do division sums in this way when the divisors are any of the numbers from 2 to 12. This is called Short Division.

Here is a rather longer example, done by the short method:
Divide 2,247 by 6.

$$
\begin{array}{r}
374 \\
6\ \overline{)2247} \\
3\ \text{remainder.}
\end{array}
$$

Answer: 374 and 3 remainder.

This would be the working, said aloud:

" (i) 6 into 22: 3, and *4* over.
  (ii) 6 into 44: 7, and *2* over.
  (iii) 6 into 27: 4, and *3* over.   Write down, 3 remainder."

When the divisors are greater than 12, use the long method.

Example.   Divide 5,863 by 27.

$$
\begin{array}{r}
217 \\
27\ \overline{)5863} \\
54 \\
\overline{46} \\
27 \\
\overline{193} \\
189 \\
\overline{4}\ \text{remainder.}
\end{array}
$$

Answer: 217 and remainder 4.

Division (money)

Example 1.   Divide £20 18s. 8d. by 7.

```
            £          s.          d.
            2          19          9
      7 | 20          18           8
        £6 ──────→ 120        ↗ 60
              7 | 138    ╱  7 | 68
                    5s.╱       5d. remainder.
```

Answer: £2 19s. 9d. and remainder 5d.

Explanation:

(i) The remainder, after dividing £20 by 7, is £6. This is converted into 120s. and put in the shillings column, as shown by the arrow, under the 18s. already there, to which it is added, making, in all, 138s.

(ii) The remainder, after dividing 138s. by 7 is 5s. This is converted into pence, and placed in the pence column under the 8d. already there, to which it is added, making in all 68d.

(iii) The remainder, after dividing 68d. by 7, is 5d.

Therefore, the answer is, as shown, £2 19s. 9d., and remainder 5d.

Example 2.   Divide £633 17s. 5d. by 26.

```
            £          s.          d.
           24           7           7
     26 | 633          17           5
          52     ↗ 180       ↗ 180
         ───   26 | 197   ╱ 26 | 185
         113      182          182
         104  ╱   ───      ╱   ───
         ───      15s.╱        3d. remainder.
         £9╱
```

Answer: £24 7s. 7d. and remainder 3d.

EXERCISE E
Division

1.   4 | 278   7 | 5834   9 | 6185   12 | 6539

2.   36 | 5962   36 | 86371   36 | 42589

3.   240 | 86592   240 | 50734   240 | 119654

4. 28)7256   43)5986   66)3286   94)116835

5. 136)86732   247)10763   152)70683   302)805691

6. 6)13s. 9d.   8)19s. 7d.   12)15s. 3d.   10)17s. 2d.

7. 9)£16 8s. 5d.   7)£14 15s. 4d.   12)£135 1s. 10d.

8. 15)£37 16s. 10d.   28)£65 12s. 9d.   36)£805 17s. 0d.

9. 52)£235 0s. 0d.   52)£400 0s. 0d.   52)£750 0s. 0d.

10. 112)£7 10s. 0d.   112)£34 15s. 0d.   112)£127 10s. 0d.

Convert into £s to the nearest £:

11. 27,462 pence; 569,246 pence; 796,384 pence.

12. 1,264,392 pence; 1,732,526 pence; 2,568,462 pence.

Convert into yards, feet and inches:

13. 758 inches; 397 inches; 868 inches; 3,241 inches.

14. 2,617 inches; 3,728 inches; 4,659 inches; 7,315 inches.

Fractions

What is a fraction?

In the Oxford Dictionary, it says:

" Fraction. A numerical quantity that is not an integer, expressed by numerator above and denominator below a line."

Thus, the following are fractions:

$$\tfrac{3}{16}; \quad \tfrac{14}{25}; \quad \tfrac{7}{8};$$

and so on.

We read these quantities as;

three-sixteenths; fourteen-twenty-fifths; seven-eighths.

How can we get three-sixteenths of anything? This can be done in two ways:

(i) Divide the thing into sixteen parts, and take three of them. Fig. 1, page 251, is a square divided into sixteen parts. Three of them are shaded, therefore, the shaded part of the square is three-sixteenths, that is, $\tfrac{3}{16}$, of the whole square.

(ii) We may take three of the things; divide each into sixteen parts, and take one of those parts from each of the squares.

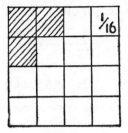

Fig. 1

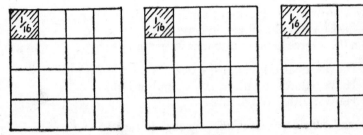

Fig. 2

If you compare Fig. 2 with Fig. 1, you will agree that three-sixteenths obtained in this way, is just the same quantity as three-sixteenths obtained by the first method.

In the same way we may regard $\frac{14}{25}$ either as something divided into 25 parts, of which 14 are taken; or as 14 of those things, each divided into 25 parts, one part being taken from each.

Sometimes we think of a fraction in the first way; sometimes, in the second way; both lead finally to the same result.

Let us calculate $\frac{3}{16}$ of £1 in both ways.

First. Find one-sixteenth of £1 and then multiply it by 3.

$$
\begin{array}{r}
\text{1s.}\qquad\quad\text{3d.} \\
16\,\overline{)\,\text{20s.}\qquad\quad \text{0d.}} \\
\text{16s.}\qquad \nearrow \text{48d.} \\
\overline{\text{4s.}}\;\nearrow\;16\,\overline{)\,\text{48d.}}
\end{array}
$$

so,
$$
\begin{aligned}
&\text{One-sixteenth of £1}=\text{1s. 3d.,} \\
&\text{three-sixteenths of £1}=\text{1s. 3d.}\times 3 \\
&=\text{3s. 9d}
\end{aligned}
$$

Secondly, find one-sixteenth of £3 (that is, of 60s.).

$$
\begin{array}{rl}
& \quad\text{3s.}\qquad\qquad\text{9d.}\\
16\,\overline{|\,}& \text{60s.}\qquad\qquad\text{0d.}\\
& \text{48s.}\qquad\quad\text{144d.}\\
\hline
& \text{12s.}\quad 16\,\overline{|\,\text{144d.}}
\end{array}
$$

In both cases, we get the same answer, namely 3s. 9d.

Addition and subtraction of fractions

Examine an ordinary scholar's ruler, 6 inches, or 12 inches long. You will probably find some of the inches divided into SIXTEENTHS; others into TWELFTHS; others into TENTHS.

From these three kinds of divisions we get three groups of fractions:

   (i) Halves, quarters, eighths, sixteenths;
   (ii) Halves, thirds, quarters, sixths, and twelfths;
   (iii) Halves, fifths, and tenths.

We shall consider each of these groups in turn.
(i) Halves, quarters, eighths, sixteenths.
People whose work involves measuring—tailors, dressmakers, upholsterers, joiners and cabinet-makers, fitters and turners, and so on—almost always work in fractions in this group, so we shall deal with them first.

Here is a copy of a ruler, 4 inches long.

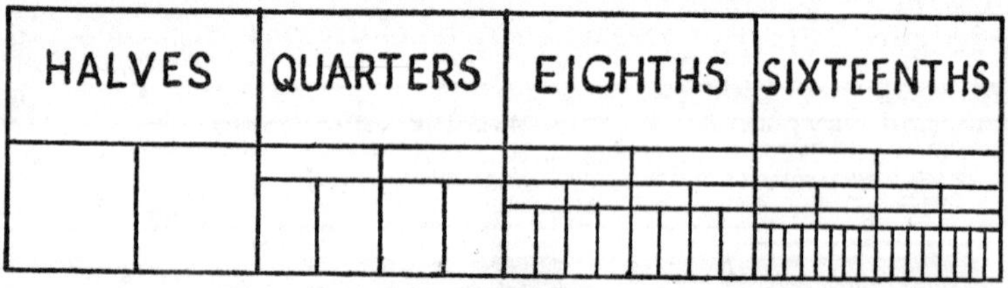

Fig. 3

The first inch is divided into halves; the second into quarters; the third into eighths; and the fourth into sixteenths.

If you wish to measure half-an-inch, you may do so by using either the half-inches in the first section of the ruler, or by taking two quarter-inches from the second section; or four eighths from the third section; or eight sixteenths from the fourth section.

In other words;

One-half = two-quarters = four-eighths = eight-sixteenths;

that is, $\frac{1}{2}=\frac{2}{4}=\frac{4}{8}=\frac{8}{16}$.

If you wish to measure one-quarter of an inch, you may use the second, third or fourth sections of the ruler. (You cannot measure one-quarter of an inch exactly with the first section.)

We see that:

One-quarter = two-eighths = four-sixteenths;

that is, $\frac{1}{4}=\frac{2}{8}=\frac{4}{16}$.

Finally, we see that:

One-eighth = two-sixteenths; that is, $\frac{1}{8}=\frac{2}{16}$.

We can now proceed to add, and to subtract, quantities involving these fractions.

Here is an addition involving halves, quarters, and eighths.

$$3\tfrac{1}{4}$$
$$2\tfrac{1}{8}$$
$$4\tfrac{1}{2}$$
$$\overline{}$$

As it stands, we may add up " mentally ". Starting from the bottom, we should say;

" one-half, that is four-eighths, and one-eighth = five eighths; and
  a quarter, that is two-eighths = seven-eighths."

Now, adding the whole ones—which make nine—we should get as the sum of the addition, nine and seven-eighths; that is $9\tfrac{7}{8}$.

If we do not want to do it mentally, we should set it down as shown below. On the right, you will see that we have expressed all the fractions as eighths.

$$3\tfrac{1}{4}=3\tfrac{2}{8}$$
$$2\tfrac{1}{8}=2\tfrac{1}{8}$$
$$4\tfrac{1}{2}=4\tfrac{4}{8}$$
$$\overline{9\tfrac{7}{8}}$$

Here is an example in which it is advisable to express all the fractions as sixteenths before we begin to add.

$$3\tfrac{3}{8}\ \ =3\tfrac{6}{16}$$
$$5\tfrac{1}{2}\ \ =5\tfrac{8}{16}$$
$$1\tfrac{3}{16}=1\tfrac{3}{16}$$
$$\overline{}$$

When we add up the sixteenths, we find that there are seventeen of them: that is, one whole one, which must be " carried ", and one-sixteenth over, which should be put in the sixteenths column. Adding the whole ones, we now find the complete sum to be ten and one-sixteenth, that is $10\frac{1}{16}$.

Here is an example in subtraction.

$$6\frac{3}{16} = 6\frac{3}{16}$$
$$2\frac{1}{2} = 2\frac{8}{16}$$

Here we have to make-up $2\frac{8}{16}$ into $6\frac{3}{16}$.

First, we make up $\frac{8}{16}$ into a whole one and $\frac{3}{16}$; to do this we need $\frac{8}{16}$, and $\frac{3}{16}$; adding we get $\frac{11}{16}$.

We now need 3 more whole ones to complete the make-up to $6\frac{8}{16}$. Thus the answer is $3\frac{11}{16}$.

(ii) Halves, thirds, quarters, sixths and twelfths.

The fractions in this group are not so frequently used in everyday-life, as those in group (i), but it is as well that we should know how to deal with them. The procedure is similar to that which we have already used.

Here is a copy of a ruler divided into halves, quarters and twelfths.

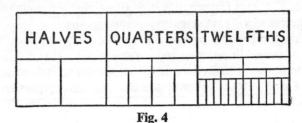

Fig. 4

From this ruler we can see at a glance how to change halves, and quarters into twelfths.

For instance:
$$\frac{1}{2} = \frac{6}{12};$$
$$\frac{1}{4} = \frac{3}{12};$$
$$\frac{3}{4} = \frac{9}{12}.$$

How many twelfths are there in one-third? Obviously, one-third of twelve parts into which the last inch is divided, is four twelfths; therefore, $\frac{1}{3} = \frac{4}{12};$
and $\frac{2}{3} = \frac{8}{12}.$

Similarly, we see that

$$\frac{1}{6} = \frac{2}{12};$$
$$\frac{5}{6} = \frac{10}{12}; \quad \text{and so on.}$$

Here is an addition sum involving these fractions, worked out completely.

$$
\begin{aligned}
2\tfrac{2}{3} &= \ 2\tfrac{8}{12} \\
5\tfrac{1}{2} &= \ 5\tfrac{6}{12} \\
1\tfrac{3}{4} &= \ 1\tfrac{9}{12} \\
4\tfrac{1}{6} &= \ 4\tfrac{2}{12} \\
\hline
& \ 14\tfrac{1}{12}
\end{aligned}
$$

Explanation.

We converted all the fractions into twelfths, then adding them we found that they came to $\frac{25}{12}$; that is,

$$\text{2 whole ones and } \tfrac{1}{12}:$$

we wrote down the $\frac{1}{12}$ in the twelfths column, and " carried " 2 to the column of whole ones. Thus we got 14 whole ones, so the sum is as shown: $14\frac{1}{12}$.

Here is a subtraction sum.

$$
\begin{aligned}
5\tfrac{7}{12} &= 5\tfrac{7}{12} \\
3\tfrac{3}{4} &= 3\tfrac{9}{12} \\
\hline
& 1\tfrac{10}{12} \quad (= 1\tfrac{5}{6}, \text{ since } \tfrac{2}{12} = \tfrac{1}{6}).
\end{aligned}
$$

(iii) Halves, fifths, and tenths.

This set of fractions is even less frequently used than those in the last group, but to complete our plan, we proceed as in the groups (i) and (ii).

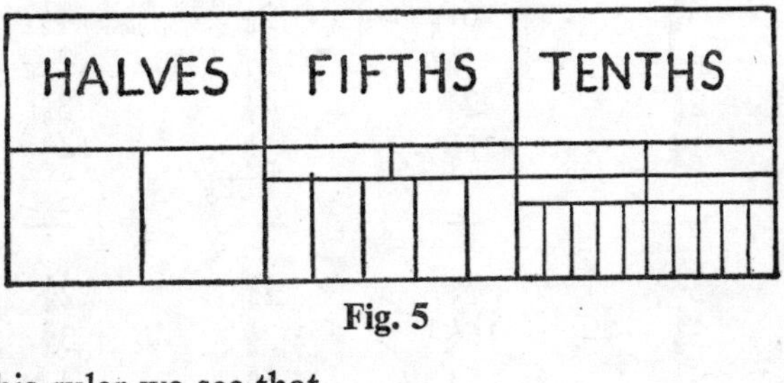

HALVES	FIFTHS	TENTHS

Fig. 5

From this ruler we see that

$$\frac{1}{2} = \frac{5}{10};$$
$$\frac{1}{5} = \frac{2}{10}.$$

Here are an addition sum—on the left, and a subtraction—on the right, involving the fractions, halves, fifths, and tenths.

Addition		Subtraction	
$2\frac{1}{2}$	$= 2\frac{5}{10}$	$9\frac{1}{5} = 9\frac{2}{10}$	
$4\frac{1}{10}$	$= 4\frac{1}{10}$	$4\frac{1}{2} = 4\frac{5}{10}$	
$3\frac{3}{5}$	$= 3\frac{6}{10}$	$\overline{4\frac{7}{10}}$	
	$\overline{10\frac{2}{10}} \quad (=10\frac{1}{5})$		

The explanation. The addition in the sum of the tenths is $\frac{12}{10}$, which is equal to one whole one to be " carried " to the column of whole ones, and $\frac{2}{10}$ which is set in the answer in the tenths column. Therefore, the complete sum is $10\frac{2}{10}$, which is equal to $10\frac{1}{5}$.

If we contrast this method of working sums involving halves, fifths and tenths, with the decimal method, we shall see which is the simpler. We write $\qquad \frac{1}{2} = \cdot5;$
$$\frac{1}{5} = \cdot2.$$

The two sums, addition and subtraction, above become, in the decimal notation:

Addition		Subtraction	
$2\frac{1}{2}$	$= 2\cdot5$	$9\frac{1}{5} = 9\cdot2$	
$4\frac{1}{10}$	$= 4\cdot1$	$4\frac{1}{2} = 4\cdot5$	
$3\frac{3}{5}$	$= 3\cdot6$	$\overline{4\cdot7}$	
	$\overline{10\cdot2}$		

EXERCISE F

Addition

1.

$3\frac{1}{2}$	$6\frac{5}{12}$	$2\frac{1}{5}$	$4\frac{1}{2}$
$4\frac{5}{16}$	$3\frac{1}{6}$	$3\frac{7}{10}$	$2\frac{7}{16}$
$2\frac{3}{8}$	$2\frac{3}{4}$	$4\frac{1}{2}$	$3\frac{7}{8}$
$1\frac{3}{4}$	$5\frac{1}{3}$	$5\frac{3}{5}$	$4\frac{3}{4}$
—	—	—	—

2.

$5\frac{15}{16}$	$7\frac{3}{8}$	$2\frac{1}{2}$	$2\frac{1}{2}$
$3\frac{1}{8}$	$16\frac{1}{4}$	$3\frac{3}{4}$	$3\frac{3}{4}$
$9\frac{1}{2}$	$5\frac{5}{8}$	$5\frac{5}{8}$	$4\frac{5}{12}$
$4\frac{3}{4}$	$6\frac{1}{2}$	$6\frac{1}{4}$	$6\frac{1}{3}$
—	—	—	—

Subtraction

3.　　$16\frac{1}{4}$　　　$12\frac{1}{8}$　　　$10\frac{1}{4}$　　　$17\frac{3}{8}$
　　　$5\frac{7}{8}$　　　$9\frac{1}{16}$　　　$6\frac{15}{16}$　　　$8\frac{3}{4}$
　　　———　　　———　　　———　　　———

4.　　$25\frac{2}{3}$　　　$13\frac{3}{4}$　　　$25\frac{1}{4}$　　　$20\frac{1}{4}$
　　　$16\frac{1}{4}$　　　$10\frac{11}{12}$　　　$16\frac{7}{12}$　　　$16\frac{2}{3}$
　　　———　　　———　　　———　　　———

5.　　$20\frac{1}{16}$　　　$14\frac{1}{4}$　　　$12\frac{7}{8}$　　　$17\frac{1}{4}$
　　　$17\frac{3}{8}$　　　$10\frac{5}{16}$　　　$9\frac{15}{16}$　　　$3\frac{5}{8}$
　　　———　　　———　　　———　　　———

Find the missing line in these additions:

6.　　$3\frac{1}{4}$　　　$2\frac{1}{12}$　　　$3\frac{1}{5}$　　　$7\frac{7}{8}$
　　　$5\frac{1}{8}$　　　$3\frac{1}{2}$　　　$4\frac{1}{2}$　　　$2\frac{3}{16}$
　　　...　　　...　　　...　　　$5\frac{1}{2}$
　　　$7\frac{1}{16}$　　　$5\frac{2}{3}$　　　$6\frac{3}{10}$　　　...
　　　$5\frac{1}{2}$　　　$7\frac{1}{4}$　　　$1\frac{3}{5}$　　　$2\frac{1}{4}$
　　　$25\frac{5}{16}$　　$21\frac{1}{12}$　　21　　　$25\frac{1}{4}$

Multiplication of fractions

I suppose that if you were asked what 3×2 means, most of you would reply: "Three-times Two" or "Two-times Three".

What would be the reply if you were asked what $\frac{3}{4} \times \frac{2}{5}$ means?

If you think for a moment you will see that it cannot mean either

$$\frac{2}{5} \text{ times } \frac{3}{4} \quad \text{ or } \quad \frac{3}{4} \text{ times } \frac{2}{5}.$$

The expression "$\frac{2}{5}$ *times* anything" is meaningless.

You cannot bounce a ball two-fifths of a time; nor can you go to the pictures two-fifths of a time. Such actions can only be done a whole number of times or not at all!

Therefore, the sign $\times$ in

$$\frac{3}{4} \times \frac{2}{5}$$

cannot mean "times".

Then what does it mean?

It is desirable that the sign should mean the same thing in both examples. We can see that it does, if we agree that both expressions represent the areas of oblongs or rectangles. Thus, if we let 3×2

represent the area of a rectangle 3 units long, and 2 units broad, then $\frac{3}{4} \times \frac{2}{5}$ would represent the area of a rectangle $\frac{3}{4}$ of a unit long, and $\frac{2}{5}$ of a unit broad.

With this meaning it is a very simple matter to find the value of
$$\frac{3}{4} \times \frac{2}{5}.$$
Before we do this, let us take a simpler example, say, find the value of
$$\frac{1}{4} \times \frac{1}{5},$$
that is, find the area of a rectangle $\frac{1}{4}$ of a unit long, and $\frac{1}{5}$ of a unit broad.   We shall take the unit to be 1 inch.

The question then becomes: What is the area of a rectangle
$$\tfrac{1}{4}'' \times \tfrac{1}{5}''?$$

Let *ABCD* be a square, sides $1''$ long.

Divide *AB* into 4 equal parts, and *AD* into 5 equal parts, then by drawing parallel lines as shown in Fig 6, we divide the square inch into 20 small rectangles.

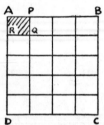

Fig. 6

Each of the small rectangles in this square is $\frac{1}{20}$ of a square inch; and each is $\frac{1}{4}'' \times \frac{1}{5}''$.

Therefore, $\frac{1}{4}'' \times \frac{1}{5}'' = \frac{1}{20}$ of a square inch.

Let us take another example.

What is the area of a rectangle $\frac{1}{2}'' \times \frac{1}{3}''$?

Draw a square *ABCD*, sides $1''$ long, and divide *AB* into 2 equal parts, and *AD* into 3 equal parts.   Draw parallel lines as in Fig. 7, thus dividing the square inch into 6 equal parts.

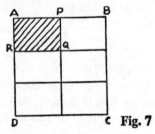

Fig. 7

Each of the small rectangles in this square is $\frac{1}{6}$ of a square inch, and each is $\frac{1}{2}'' \times \frac{1}{3}''$.

Therefore, $\frac{1}{2}'' \times \frac{1}{3}'' = \frac{1}{6}$ of a square inch.

From these two examples, you may see a rule for finding the answer. In each case the numerator of the fraction in the answer is the product of the two separate numerators, namely

$$1 \times 1 = 1,$$

and the denominator of the fraction in the answer is the product of the two separate denominators. In the first case it was

$$4 \times 5 = 20; \quad \text{so} \quad \frac{1}{4} \times \frac{1}{5} = \frac{1}{20};$$

and in the second case it was

$$2 \times 3 = 6; \quad \text{so} \quad \frac{1}{2} \times \frac{1}{3} = \frac{1}{6}.$$

Let us now return to the question proposed on page 259, namely: What is the area of a rectangle $\frac{3}{4}'' \times \frac{2}{5}''$?

Draw a square, $ABCD$, sides $1''$ long. Divide AB into 4 equal parts, and AD into 5 equal parts. Draw parallel lines, as in Fig. 6, page 259, thus dividing the square into 20 equal rectangles, each $\frac{1}{20}$ of a square inch in area (Fig. 8).

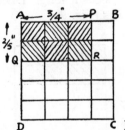

Fig. 8

Choose the point P in AB so that $AP = \frac{3}{4}''$ and the point Q in AD so that $AQ = \frac{2}{5}''$. Then, the rectangle $APRQ$ is $\frac{3}{4}'' \times \frac{2}{5}''$. In it, shown by shading, there are 2 rows of the small rectangles, each row containing 3 of those rectangles; that is, altogether there are 3×2 of the small rectangles in it.

Now, each small rectangle $= \frac{1}{20}$ of a square inch,

therefore, the rectangle $\frac{3}{4}'' \times \frac{2}{5}'' = \dfrac{3 \times 2}{20}$ of a square inch

$$= \tfrac{6}{20} \text{ of a square inch.}$$

Here, the numerator in the answer is the product of the numerators of the separate fractions, and, as we saw before, the denominator is

s   D.L.M.

the product of the separate denominators; thus we may use this rule:

To find the product of two fractions, divide the product of the two numerators by the product of the two denominators.

Thus,

$$\frac{3}{4} \times \frac{2}{5} = \frac{3 \times 2}{4 \times 5}$$

$$= \frac{6}{20}.$$

Here is another example to be worked by the rule. Find the product $\frac{3}{4} \times \frac{1}{5}$.

$$\frac{3}{4} \times \frac{1}{5} = \frac{3 \times 1}{4 \times 5}$$

$$= \frac{3}{20}.$$

We saw on page 250 how to find a fraction of something; for instance, $\frac{3}{16}$ of £1.

It may be necessary to calculate a fraction of a fraction of something; for instance, $\frac{3}{4}$ of $\frac{2}{5}$ of something, say, $\frac{3}{4}$ of $\frac{2}{5}$ of a square inch.

Draw a square $ABCD$, sides 1″ long. Divide AB into 4 equal parts, and AD into 5 equal parts (Fig. 9)

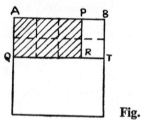

Fig. 9

Choose the point Q in AD so that $AQ = \frac{2}{5}''$.

Draw QT parallel to AB, cutting BC at the point T; then, the rectangle $ABTQ = \frac{2}{5}$ of a square inch.

Choose the point P in AB so that $AP = \frac{3}{4}''$.

Draw PR parallel to AD, cutting QT at the point R; then the rectangle $APRQ = \frac{3}{4}$ of the rectangle $ABTQ$

$$= \frac{3}{4} \text{ of } \frac{2}{5} \text{ of a square inch.}$$

Now, the rectangle $APRQ$ is $\frac{3}{4}'' \times \frac{2}{5}''$, therefore, $\frac{3}{4}$ of $\frac{2}{5}$ of a square inch

$$= \text{a rectangle } \frac{3}{4}'' \times \frac{2}{5}''$$

$$= \frac{6}{20} \text{ of a square inch;}$$

therefore, in calculating a fraction of a fraction of something we can use the same rule as we used for finding the product of two fractions, namely, divide the product of the numerators of the separate fractions by the product of the denominators of the fractions.

Here is another example to be worked by the rule.

Calculate $\frac{2}{5}$ of $\frac{3}{4}$ of something.

$$\frac{2}{5} \text{ of } \frac{3}{4} \text{ of something} = \frac{2 \times 3}{5 \times 4} \text{ of that thing;}$$

$$= \frac{6}{20} \text{ of that thing.}$$

The process of cancelling

Returning to the ruler graduated in sixteenths of an inch on page 252, we see that

$$\frac{12}{16} = \frac{3}{4}.$$

We might have written

$$\frac{12}{16} = \frac{3 \text{ groups of 4 sixteenths}}{4 \text{ groups of 4 sixteenths}};$$

but instead of doing this in full we say:

" Cancel numerator and denominator by 4 ", that is, divide the numerator and the denominator by 4, and write the process thus:

$$\overset{3}{\underset{4}{\frac{12}{16}}} = \frac{3}{4}.$$

In the same way, we see from the ruler that

$$\frac{6}{8} = \frac{3}{4}.$$

Here we see that both the numerator and the denominator of the fraction on the left-hand side of the equation can be grouped in twos. Therefore, we " cancel numerator and denominator by 2 "; or, more briefly, " cancel by 2 ", and we get

$$\overset{3}{\underset{4}{\frac{6}{8}}} = \frac{3}{4}.$$

Similarly, $\dfrac{\overset{2}{\cancel{10}}}{\underset{5}{\cancel{25}}}=\dfrac{2}{5}$ (cancelling by 5);

and $\dfrac{\overset{2}{\cancel{12}}}{\underset{3}{\cancel{18}}}=\dfrac{2}{3}$ (cancelling by 6).

We found on page 259 that the area of the rectangle

$\tfrac{2}{5}'' \times \tfrac{3}{4}'' = \tfrac{6}{20}$ of a square inch.

We may cancel in this fraction by 2, and we get

$$\dfrac{\overset{3}{\cancel{6}}}{\underset{10}{\cancel{20}}}=\dfrac{3}{10}\,.$$

It is customary to cancel in the early stages, as follows:

Notice that one of the numerators is 2; and that one of the denominators, 4, will divide by 2: that is why we cancel by 2;

$$\dfrac{2}{5}\times\dfrac{\overset{1}{\cancel{3}}}{\underset{2}{\cancel{4}}}=\dfrac{1\times3}{5\times2}=\dfrac{3}{10}\,.$$

We usually omit the stage $\dfrac{1\times3}{5\times2}$, and write directly $\dfrac{3}{10}\,.$

The cancelling process is equivalent to stating that,

a rectangle $\tfrac{2}{5}'' \times \tfrac{3}{4}''$ is equal to a rectangle $\tfrac{1}{5}'' \times \tfrac{3}{2}''$.

That this is true may be seen from the following diagrams. Fig. 10 is $\tfrac{2}{5}'' \times \tfrac{3}{4}''$; Fig. 11 is half the breadth of this, but double its length, that is $\tfrac{1}{5}'' \times \tfrac{3}{2}''$.

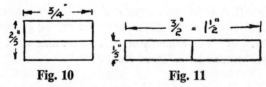

Fig. 10   Fig. 11

Thus, when finding the product of two—or more—fractions we cancel numerator and denominator of any of the single fractions or the numerator of one fraction and the denominator of another.

Division of fractions

As in the case of multiplication of fractions, we shall find a method of division based on the area of a rectangle.

If the area of a rectangle be 6 square inches, and its breadth 2 inches, its length in inches will be $6 \div 2$.

In the same way, in a rectangle containing, say, $1\frac{1}{2}$ square inches and $\frac{2}{3}''$ broad, the length in inches will be $1\frac{1}{2} \div \frac{2}{3}$.

Let us find the length in a practical way.

(i) Draw a rectangle containing $1\frac{1}{2}$ square inches; that is, a rectangle $1\frac{1}{2}$ inches long, 1 inch broad (Fig. 12).

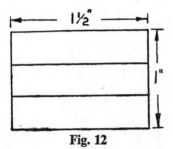

Fig. 12

(ii) Cut this rectangle into three equal rectangles, each $\frac{1}{3}''$ broad, and place them end to end (Fig. 13).   The length of this rectangle is $4\frac{1}{2}''$ (that is, $1\frac{1}{2}'' \times 3''$).

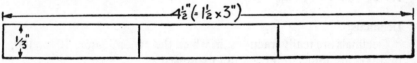

Fig. 13

(iii) Now cut this rectangle into two equal rectangles, each $2\frac{1}{4}''$ (that is $\frac{1}{2}$ of $4\frac{1}{2}''$) long, and place them side by side (Fig. 14). This rectangle is $1\frac{1}{2}$ sq. ins. in area; and its breadth is $\frac{2}{3}''$. Its length is $2\frac{1}{4}$ inches. Therefore,

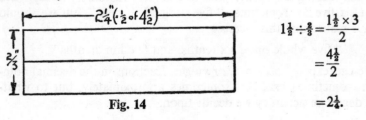

Fig. 14

$$1\frac{1}{2} \div \frac{2}{3} = \frac{1\frac{1}{2} \times 3}{2}$$

$$= \frac{4\frac{1}{2}}{2}$$

$$= 2\frac{1}{4}.$$

EXERCISE G

Multiplication and Division

1. $\frac{2}{3} \times \frac{5}{8}$; $\frac{3}{4} \times \frac{3}{5}$; $\frac{3}{7} \times \frac{1}{8}$; $\frac{6}{7} \times \frac{3}{2}$.

2. $\frac{9}{8} \times \frac{4}{3}$; $1\frac{1}{8} \times \frac{1}{6}$; $\frac{7}{8} \times 1\frac{1}{3}$; $1\frac{1}{3} \times 1\frac{7}{8}$.

3. $\frac{1}{3}$ of $\frac{3}{4}$ of a square inch; $\frac{1}{2}$ of $\frac{1}{4}$ of 2 lb.

4. $\frac{1}{3}$ of $\frac{1}{2}$ of a square yard, $\frac{2}{3}$ of $\frac{5}{6}$ of £1.

5. $4\frac{5}{16}'' \times 7$; $2\frac{3}{4}'' \times 9$; $4\frac{1}{4}'' \times 1\frac{1}{2}$.

6. $3\frac{2}{3}'' \times 8$; $4\frac{1}{12}'' \times 20$; $7\frac{5}{8}'' \times 2\frac{1}{2}$.

7. $\frac{1}{2}(2\frac{1}{4} \times 1\frac{1}{2})$; $\frac{1}{4}(1\frac{1}{8} \times 2\frac{1}{2})$; $\frac{1}{3}(\frac{3}{4} \times 1\frac{1}{3})$.

8. $\frac{3}{4}(1\frac{3}{5} \times \frac{1}{2})$; $\frac{1}{8}(1\frac{1}{2} \times 4)$; $(\frac{1}{3} \times 1\frac{1}{8}) \times 1\frac{1}{4}$.

9. $3(2\frac{1}{2} \times 1\frac{1}{2})$; $2(1\frac{1}{4} \times \frac{3}{5})$; $1\frac{1}{8}(1\frac{1}{3} \times \frac{1}{2})$.

10. $\frac{1}{3}(\frac{1}{2} \times 1\frac{3}{5})$; $3(2\frac{1}{3} \times 1\frac{1}{2})$; $4(1\frac{1}{4} \times \frac{2}{3})$.

11. $1\frac{1}{4} \div \frac{2}{3}$; $\frac{7}{8} \div \frac{2}{3}$; $\frac{3}{4} \div \frac{2}{3}$.

12. $1\frac{1}{2} \div \frac{3}{4}$; $2\frac{1}{2} \div \frac{3}{5}$; $1\frac{1}{3} \div \frac{2}{5}$.

13. $2\frac{1}{2} \div \frac{5}{16}$; $1\frac{1}{2} \div \frac{3}{8}$; $1\frac{3}{4} \div \frac{7}{12}$.

14. $5\frac{1}{3} \div \frac{4}{5}$; $6\frac{3}{4} \div \frac{2}{3}$; $1\frac{1}{8} \div \frac{3}{8}$.

15. $2\frac{1}{4} \div \frac{2}{3}$; $1\frac{1}{3} \div \frac{3}{4}$; $2\frac{2}{3} \div \frac{5}{8}$.

Decimals

Decimals are really fractions, in which the denominators 10, or 100, or 1,000 are understood but not expressed.

For instance,

$$\frac{3}{10} \text{ is written } \cdot3,$$
$$\frac{3}{100} \text{ is written } \cdot03.$$

The sum of $\frac{3}{10}$ and $\frac{3}{100}$ is written $\cdot33$.

When reading a quantity, such as $5\cdot65$, it is customary to say " five point six five ": sometimes " five decimal six five ", but we should always realise that this means

" five whole ones, six tenths, and five hundredths ".

We can express ordinary, or vulgar, fractions in the decimal notation: sometimes exactly; sometimes approximately, but to whatever degree of accuracy we decide upon.

In dealing with inches, a draughtsman could not draw to a greater degree of accuracy than the " nearest hundredth of an inch ", but a turner, using a very accurate measuring instrument called a micrometer, works to the nearest " thou ", as he calls it, meaning to the nearest " thousandth ".

Let us now express a few fractions as decimals.

Example 1. Express $\frac{3}{4}$ as a decimal to the nearest hundredth.

$\frac{3}{4}$ means, as we saw on page 251, 3 *whole ones* ÷4.

Since we want the answer to the nearest hundredth, we turn the whole ones into hundredths: that is, 300 hundredths and then divide by 4.

$$\begin{array}{r} 75 \text{ hundredths, exactly} \\ \overline{4\,|\,300 \text{ hundredths}} \end{array}$$

so, $\frac{3}{4} = 75$ hundredths
           $= \cdot 75$.

Example 2. Express $\frac{5}{8}$ as a decimal to the nearest thousandth.
In 5 whole ones, there are 5,000 thousandths.

$$\begin{array}{r} 625 \text{ thousandths, exactly} \\ \overline{8\,|\,5000 \text{ thousandths}} \end{array}$$

Therefore, $\frac{5}{8} = 625$ thousandths
                 $= \cdot 625$.

We do not always go through the whole of the working shown above; we proceed as follows:

Example 3. Express $\frac{7}{15}$ as a decimal, to the nearest thousandth.
We have to divide 7 whole ones by 15.

$$\begin{array}{r} 0 \cdot 466 \\ 15\,\overline{\smash{)}\,7 \cdot 0} \\ 6\,0 \\ \hline 1\,00 \\ 90 \\ \hline 100 \\ 90 \\ \hline \dot{1}0 \end{array}$$

Explanation.

We say " 15 into 7: it won't go; put a 0 in the answer, followed by the decimal point.

" Bring down a 0.

" 15 into 70 goes 4; put 4 after the decimal point in the answer; $4 \times 15 = 60$; and so on."

The rest of the working is like straightforward division.

Multiplication of decimals

The simplest multipliers are 10, 100, 1,000 and so on.

Multiply 15·2 by 10.

$$
\begin{array}{r}
15 \cdot 2 \\
10 \\
\hline
152 \cdot 0 \\
\end{array}
$$

We see that the digits are unaltered; their positions only are changed; each is moved one place to the left.

Multiply 15·2 by 100.

It will be sufficient if we multiply the answer to the previous example by 10, that is, we must slide the digits one more place to the left.

The answer is thus: 1520·0.

Therefore, we get the rules:

To multiply a decimal by 10 slide the digits one place to the left;

To multiply by 100, slide the digits two places to the left;

and so on.

It follows that if we wish to multiply by 20, we multiply by 2 and slide the digits one place to the left; to multiply by 300, we multiply by 3 and slide the digits two places to the left, and so on.

Multiply $127 \cdot 53 \times 32$.

Set the working down like this:

$$
\begin{array}{r}
127 \cdot 53 \\
32 \\
\hline
3825 \cdot 9 \\
255 \cdot 06 \\
\hline
4080 \cdot 96 \quad \text{Answer.} \\
\end{array}
$$

Note. We have multiplied by the 30 as the first step; to do this we multiplied by 3 and moved the digits one place to the left.

The method of multiplying when the multiplier contains a decimal will be understood from the following example:

Calculate the area of the rectangle 2·4″ × 1·2″.

Draw the rectangle on squared paper (Fig. 15). Divide it as shown below into two rectangles, 1″ broad, and 0·2″ broad, by the line *PQ*.

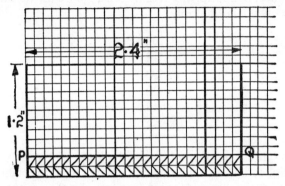

Fig. 15

The area above the line *PQ* = 2·4 square inches.

The area below the line *PQ* = 0·48 of a square inch, because each of the shaded strips, 1″ long × 0·1″ broad is one-tenth of a square inch in area; and each of the small squares to the right of the shaded strips is one-hundredth of a square inch in area.

Therefore,   the total area = 2·88 of a square inch.

This is how the sum would be set down without the diagram:

$$
\begin{array}{l}
2{\cdot}4\ \times \\
\underline{1{\cdot}2} \\
2{\cdot}4 \\
\underline{{\cdot}48} \quad \text{(that is, multiply by 2 and slide the digits one} \\
2{\cdot}88 \qquad\qquad \text{place to the right.)}
\end{array}
$$

Here is another way of calculating the area of the rectangle 2·4″ × 1·2″.

In the rectangle there are 12 rows of small squares; in each row there are 24 small squares. Therefore the total number of small squares in the rectangle is 24 × 12, that is, 288. Now each small square is one-hundredth of a square inch, so

288 small squares = 2·88 square inches;

the same result as we got by the other method. The easiest and safest way, therefore, of performing multiplication of decimals is this:

Ignore the decimal points in the multiplier and in the multiplicand, and multiply as in ordinary multiplication; then insert the decimal point in the answer after counting from the total number of decimal places in the two numbers being multiplied.

For instance, in multiplying 16·2 by 3·14, ignore the decimal points in both numbers and multiply.

$$\begin{array}{r} 162 \times 314 \\ 314 \\ \hline 48600 \\ 1620 \\ 648 \\ \hline 50868 \end{array}$$

Now, the total number of decimal places in the two numbers being multiplied is 3, so, counting three digits from the right towards the left, place the decimal point between the 0 and the 8. The answer then reads; 50·868.

Therefore,   16·2 × 3·14 = 50·868.

Division of decimals

There are many methods of dividing by a decimal; all of them have drawbacks; none of them is quite so simple as multiplication.

The difficulty always is to tell where the decimal point is to be put in the answer.

The safest method is to make a short approximate calculation before dividing by the quantities given. For example, suppose we want to divide 26·4 by 3·14 to the nearest tenth, we say:

the answer lies between 26 ÷ 3, which is a little more than 8; and 26 ÷ 4, which is a little more than 6.

Therefore, there will be only one digit to the left of the decimal point, and since the answer is to be found to the nearest tenth of an inch there will be two digits in the answer, separated by the decimal point.

We now disregard the decimal points in the divisor and dividend, and divide as in ordinary division, remembering, of course, to put the decimal point after the first digit in the answer.

$$314 \overline{\smash{)}264}$$

Set down as above, we see that 314 will not divide into 264, so we " bring down a 0 " and the division then proceeds:

$$
\begin{array}{r}
8\cdot4 \\
314\,\overline{\smash{)}\,2640} \\
2512 \\
\hline
1280 \\
1256 \\
\hline
24
\end{array}
$$

Therefore, to the nearest tenth, $26\cdot4 \div 3\cdot14 = 8\cdot4$.

EXERCISE H

1. $2\cdot5 \times 1\cdot3$; $2\cdot8 \times 1\cdot6$; $3\cdot2 \times 1\cdot9$; $2\cdot7 \times 2\cdot2$.

2. $4\cdot7 \times 2\cdot3$; $3\cdot5 \times 2\cdot9$; $5\cdot1 \times 3\cdot7$; $6\cdot3 \times 4\cdot5$.

3. $15\cdot2 \times 14\cdot5$; $27\cdot6 \times 16\cdot3$; $43\cdot8 \times 18\cdot9$; $39\cdot6 \times 17\cdot4$.

4. $15\cdot5 \times 3\cdot14$; $32\cdot6 \times 3\cdot14$; $53\cdot7 \times 3\cdot14$; $25\cdot4 \times 3\cdot14$.

5. $14\cdot2 \times 2\cdot53$; $6\cdot32 \times 2\cdot53$; $8\cdot63 \times 2\cdot53$; $9\cdot24 \times 2\cdot53$.

Answer to the nearest tenth:

6. $\dfrac{9\cdot34}{2\cdot7}$; $\dfrac{3\cdot42}{1\cdot6}$; $\dfrac{5\cdot83}{2\cdot5}$; $\dfrac{7\cdot64}{1\cdot9}$.

7. $\dfrac{16\cdot53}{5\cdot8}$; $\dfrac{21\cdot94}{6\cdot9}$; $\dfrac{24\cdot62}{3\cdot9}$; $\dfrac{32\cdot57}{6\cdot4}$.

8. $\dfrac{12\cdot64}{9\cdot8}$; $\dfrac{46\cdot37}{10\cdot8}$; $\dfrac{14\cdot52}{1\cdot6}$; $\dfrac{53\cdot86}{14\cdot9}$.

9. $\dfrac{28\cdot37}{3\cdot8}$; $\dfrac{30\cdot08}{17\cdot2}$; $\dfrac{156\cdot46}{27\cdot3}$; $\dfrac{209\cdot27}{16\cdot3}$.

10. $\dfrac{147\cdot62}{3\cdot14}$; $\dfrac{28\cdot36}{3\cdot14}$; $\dfrac{15\cdot62}{6\cdot23}$; $\dfrac{28\cdot53}{6\cdot4}$.

USEFUL INFORMATION FOR REFERENCE

1 yard.................= 36 inches   1 mile..........= 1760 yards

1 square foot........= 144 square inches

1 cubic foot..........= 1728 cubic inches

1 cubic yard.........= 27 cubic feet

1 gallon...............= 8 pints

1 quart................= one quarter of a gallon
                   = 2 pints

1 pound...............= 16 ounces
1 stone................= 14 pounds
1 hundredweight..= 112 pounds
                   = 8 stones
1 ton...................= 20 hundredweights

Air-space, and gas, are measured in cubic feet

Every Adult Person, in a room, needs at least 1000 cubic feet
of Fresh Air per hour.

The Length of the Longest Day = 16 hours 50 minutes in London
      (21st June)   = 17 hours 50 minutes in Aberdeen
The Length of the Shortest Day = 7 hours 50 minutes in London
      (22nd December)   6 hours 45 minutes in Aberdeen

In a circle there are 360 degrees

The Circumference of a circle = $3\frac{1}{7}$ times the Diameter
                          = 3·14 × diameter

The distance round the Earth = 25 thousand miles

The three angles of a triangle together equal 180 degrees.

Set Squares: In a 45-degree set square ⊿° the two shorter sides
             are equal in length.
             In a 60-degree (or 30-degree) set square ⊿° the
             longest side is double the length of the shortest side.

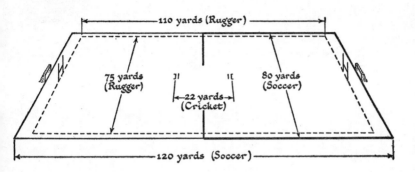

1 acre..= 4840 square yards
　　　　　　　　　　　　　　　　= a field 80 yds. × 60 yds. (approx.)
　　　　　　　　　　　　　　　　(see area above within thick lines)

The Length of a Cricket Pitch = 22 yds. (1 chain) between the stumps

An Association Football Pitch = 120 yards × 80 yards
　　　　　　　　　　　　　　= nearly 2 acres
　　　　　　　　　　　　　　(see the whole area above)

A Rugby Football Pitch...........= 110 yards × 75 yards
　　　　　　　　　　　　　　= nearly $1\frac{3}{4}$ acres
　　　　　　　　　　　　　　(see area above within dotted lines)

INDEX